LIVING IN TUNE
WITH YOUR
LIGHT
THROUGH
RESONANCE REPATTERNING

BOOKS AND HOME STUDY COURSES
BY CHLOE FAITH WORDSWORTH

See ResonanceRepatterning.net for all Home Study Courses

The Resonance Repatterning® Series

- The Fundamentals of Resonance Repatterning
  Home Study Course: "The A–Z of muscle checking"

- Transforming Primary Patterns

- Transforming Unconscious Patterns

- Resonance Repatterning Process Guide

- Transforming Chakra Patterns
  Home Study Course: "Polarity Principles and Contacts"

- Transforming Five Element and Meridian Patterns

- Inner Cultivation through the Twelve Meridians
  Home Study Course available

- Principles of Relationship
  Home Study Course available

- A New Vision

- Energetics of Relationship
  Home Study Course available

Living in Tune Series

- Living in Tune with Your Light

Resonance Repatterning® Books

- Quantum Change Made Easy

- Spiral Up! 127 Energizing Options to be your best right now

- Commitment to Life: A program for super health and vitality

LIVING IN TUNE WITH YOUR LIGHT
THROUGH
RESONANCE REPATTERNING

CHLOE FAITH WORDSWORTH

Founder and Developer of the Resonance Repatterning® System

Resonance Publishing
A Division of the Resonance Repatterning Institute, LLC
P.O. Box 4578
Scottsdale, Arizona 85261, USA
ResonanceRepatterning.net
info@ResonanceRepatterning.net

The information in this book is intended for research and educational purposes only. The author does not present any part of this work, directly or indirectly, for the diagnosis or prescription of any disease or condition. People who use the information in this book, or receive sessions from Resonance Repatterning practitioners, take responsibility for consulting the health professional of their choice regarding all matters pertaining to their physical and mental health.

Those who attend the Resonance Repatterning seminars use this material for themselves, for friends and/or professionally, in accordance with the laws of their country.

Cover photo: Rose Jones, UK – River Lea at sunrise. Every attempt has been made to contact Rose Jones for permission.

First Edition   2017
19 18 17   9 8 7 6 5 4 3 2 1   III II I
ISBN 978-1-937710-23-1
Printed in USA

CONTENTS

WHAT LIVING IN TUNE WITH YOUR LIGHT IS ABOUT

In 2008 I created fifty-two web radio shows called LIVING IN TUNE.

Half the shows were interviews with interesting people who are making a difference in the field of alternative health (you can still listen to these interviews, free of charge, by going to ResonanceRepatterning.net).

The other half of the shows consisted of inspiring, deeply moving true stories, followed by my thoughts on how we can apply the lessons of these stories in our daily life. The shows included a Resonance Repatterning process, which I gave to someone who phoned in for a Resonance Repatterning session with me.

After I completed the fifty-two shows, I placed LIVING IN TUNE on the back burner, deciding that one day I would put the twenty-six stories and Repatternings into three books. But for nine years the project remained on the bottom of my long To Do list. Finally, one of the Resonance Repatterning teachers in Mexico begged me to create a new seminar from the LIVING IN TUNE shows. I said, "OK, one day." A week later a Resonance Repatterning practitioner emailed me about the LIVING IN TUNE Weight Repatterning: "What an awesome and life-transforming experience for me! I have battled with extra weight much of my life."

Her email made me curious and for the first time in nine years I opened up this particular show and read its story and the Repatterning. And that was it. The LIVING IN TUNE web radio shows went to the top of my project list and that very day I started to edit and update the material for the first of the three LIVING IN TUNE books: LIVING IN TUNE WITH YOUR LIGHT.

As I read and re-read the eight stories that became a part of this first book, I found myself moved to tears. What I realized is that stories are important – for our self-healing, for when the going gets tough in our life, for when we need uplift.

Like ancient Greek myths, stories have been told and re-told since the beginning of time, with multiple variations depending on the teller and the audience listening to the story.

Why do we need these stories, whoever we are and whatever our age?

• They are a vehicle for carrying values of the spirit

• They let us know that greatness of mind and spirit is possible

• They teach us important lessons

• They inspire us to reach beyond our normal routine lives

• The best stories teach us how to live

Stories activate our symbolic, creative, intuitive, imaginative right cerebral hemisphere. This is why we create stories out of everything that happens to us, why each day we tell family members the story of what we have done that day, why children share the ups and downs of their day with their parents. We all want to tell our story and we want our story to be heard.

Our right brain needs stories, which is why we are addicted to stories in books and films and why in ancient times around the world, story tellers passed down their people's myths from generation to generation.

In this book I have chosen eight true stories that represent people who discovered their inner light, radiated their light and survived through the power of their light.

As has been known for thousands of years in India and China, we are beings of light. And bio-physicists are now discovering that each of our millions of cells actually radiates light. When this light is coherent, it transmits positive coherent information to our body and mind. When our light is non-coherent, it transmits negative non-coherent information.

The eight stories and the eight Resonance Repatterning processes in this book are about helping our body-mind system transmit positive coherent information for our transformation and self-mastery.

What Resonance Repatterning is about

Coherence is when we are in sync with what is life-giving (relaxation, pleasure, focus, self-worth, high energy, etc.). Non-coherence is when we are out of sync with what is life-giving (tension, stress, anger, fear, depression, etc). Resonance Repatterning enables us to transform the unconscious beliefs and feelings we resonate with that manifest as any non-coherent problem we may have.

What we resonate with is what we experience. What we do not resonate with, no matter how positive it may be, we do not experience. When we resonate with what is positive and energizing within ourselves – and we no longer resonate with what is de-energizing – our life reflects this positive change. Resonance Repatterning simply offers a method for resonating with what is positive and energizing and people experience the results of their RR sessions in unexpected and even extraordinary ways.

Many experience a sense of joy – sometimes for the first time in their life. Someone with headaches may be free of pain; another who was depressed or afraid feels a sense of uplift; a problem that felt insurmountable is now seen from a new perspective. Some changes are dramatic, others are subtle, some take place immediately, others take more time. But almost everyone is deeply impressed and even awed by the Resonance Repatterning sessions they receive.

LIVING IN TUNE WITH YOUR LIGHT is not a conventional self-help book as such. The muscle checking cues in this book's Repatternings – (**mcs**) and *[**cr**] – are specifically for practitioners of Resonance Repatterning who use the processes in this book on themselves or for their clients.

Learning the complete Resonance Repatterning system for doing sessions on oneself or others takes training. For those who have not studied Resonance Repatterning, this book has much to offer:

- The stories and how they apply to you may be helpful or even life-changing.

- You can also read the statements in the Repatterning associated with each story and gain a certain understanding of yourself, your problems, your dreams and your life.

- And after each Repatterning there is a page giving suggestions on how you can use the Repatterning in your daily life.

If you read a particular Repatterning and feel it would be helpful for you, you are welcome to go to ResonanceRepatterning.net > SESSIONS for the list of RR practitioners who choose to list their name on the Institute website.

The training in Resonance Repatterning is open to anyone who is interested in their own growth and in supporting family members and friends, or for those with a professional interest in Practitioner Certification and Advanced Practitioner Certification by the Resonance Repatterning Institute.

For those who would love to learn Resonance Repatterning in person or online with Home Study support, you are welcome to check the seminar schedule at ResonanceRepatterning.net > SEMINARS. And anyone is welcome to take the HOME STUDY courses: ResonanceRepatterning.net > HOME STUDY.

In the meantime, for all those longing for something more, something higher, a way to acknowledge the light within, this book is for you.

Chloe Faith Wordsworth
Scottsdale, Arizona
October 2017

1. THE CRACK IN THE VASE – AND THE SECRET IT HOLDS

When the higher incorporates the lower into its service,
the nature of the lower is transformed into that of the higher.

Meister Eckhart

A new understanding

When we are upset, our first reaction is usually to go into anger.

In Chinese acupuncture anger is associated with the Wood Element – the frequency that is also associated with springtime, new life, hope, new beginnings, a new vision of things, growth, change, creating goals, the ability to plan and achieve our goals and with realizing our potential.

Anger, then, is a symptom of frustration when we are blocked from achieving our goals, when we can't see where we are going, when we aren't changing and growing towards our vision of what is possible or realizing our potential. In fact, we feel there isn't much to feel hopeful about.

STORY OF THE CRACK IN THE VASE

Dr. Rachel Remen in her book *Kitchen Table Wisdom* tells a story about the angriest person she had ever worked with. The young man's story has much to teach us about the secret anger holds for each one of us and the importance of finding and living our purpose.

The young man Rachel Remen was counseling had everything: he was handsome, he was a college athlete, he received respect from his admirers, he went out with beautiful women, he drove fast cars.

But two weeks after being diagnosed with osteogenic sarcoma, his right leg was amputated above the knee. His life was saved, but life felt over for him. He turned to drink and drugs, had one car accident after another and became isolated from his friends. Finally his coach recommended that he see Rachel.

In their second meeting Rachel gave him a piece of paper and asked him to draw a picture of his body. He drew the bare outline of a vase and then with a black crayon he created a deep crack through its center, ripping the paper as he scratched over the crack again and again, making it deeper. Clearly the vase was broken and could never be used again.

Gradually over the weeks he began to change, little by little. He would bring in articles and newspaper excerpts about accidents: a motorcyclist losing his leg; a girl who had been burned; a boy whose hand had been partly destroyed in an explosion. And always he would vilify the doctors and parents because none of them understood how to help people who were suffering in this way.

Rachel then asked him if there was anything he wanted to do about them. He said no, but before leaving her office he turned back and asked if she could arrange for him to meet people like this who had suffered these injuries. A few weeks later he began to visit young people in the hospital where Rachel worked who had similar problems to his.

He quickly found that he was able to reach these people of his own age group in a way that adults, parents and doctors couldn't. Then he began to talk to doctors and parents, helping them understand what people needed who had lost parts of themselves and their former lives – and the surgeons, thrilled with the results of his visits, began referring more people to him.

One of his visits was to a young woman. Her mother, sister and cousin had all died as a result of breast cancer and she had decided to have both her breasts removed surgically. She was deeply depressed and lay in bed with her eyes closed. The young man was wearing shorts with his artificial leg in full view, but he was unable to get any response from her at all, no matter what he said.

Finally, totally frustrated, he unstrapped the harness of his artificial leg, which fell to the floor with a thump. The young woman, startled, opened her eyes and saw him for the first time. The young man began snapping his fingers to the rock music that was playing on her radio, hopping round the room and laughing. After a moment she burst out laughing. The connection was made.

Later, as friends, they both began visiting people in the hospital together. She encouraged him to return to school and continue with his mission of helping people in their suffering. Eventually she became his wife.

In his final session with Rachel, they reviewed his journey. Then Rachel pulled out the picture he had drawn of himself two years before: the cracked vase. He looked at the picture and then said, 'You know, it's not finished.' Taking a crayon he began drawing thick yellow lines from the crack, radiating outward to the edge of the paper. Rachel looked on, puzzled. He smiled and put his finger on the crack and told her, "This is where the light comes through."

Such a beautiful story. A crack, which represents a loss or something destroyed, becomes the opening for the light of higher consciousness to shine through.

Anger

When we remain **stuck in our anger,** we see only our wound, our pain and suffering. When we go where the anger points us to, we find the light of a new vision, a new hope and new possibilities for living. We reconnect to our higher awareness and for the first time see our light, radiating outward to touch all who are in need.

Fear

The same applies to our other emotional reactions. When we are **stuck in fear** we see only contraction, limitation and an inability to move forward into life. When we go where the fear points us to, we find our power – not power over others, but a power that gives courage to others, that reassures and empowers others to unlock their inner strength to live from the light of their essential nature.

Jealousy

When we are **stuck in jealousy**, we see only loss and inadequacy – that others have what we want and will never have. Our view of life is in terms of better or worse, some have more and others less, and we live in the 'worse' and 'less' category. As a result, we feel weak, inadequate, unattractive and inferior. But when we go where jealousy points us to, we find our unique self – already perfect and with its own unique attractive force. We don't need to have what others have, because we are enough just as we are. We begin to accept and appreciate the light of who we are and radiate our light.

Our four brains

Let's take a look at our three brains and the relatively recent development (in the last 40,000 years) of our fourth brain.

By understanding the brain we can see why and when our emotions become destructive, and find the new possibility our negative feelings hold for us – the light radiating from the cracked vase. When we live with anger, fear and jealousy, we are living in the fight-flight survival adrenaline response of our reptilian and limbic brain and we lose the possibility to live fully from our fourth brain – the prefrontal cortex.

The reptilian brain

Our first and oldest brain is the reptilian brain – hundreds of millions of years in the making and perfecting. The reptilian brain is the first brain to develop in utero, during the first trimester after conception. Its function is survival of the species – fight (be the predator), flight (avoid being eaten by a predator), and mate (keep the species going)!

The reptilian brain helps us create survival strategies. Like every animal, when we feel threatened, we react instinctively – without feelings or the constraints of our conscience. Our reptilian brain has no ethical sense: we do whatever it takes to survive and maintain our physical well-being.

It is interesting looking at the corporate and political arena from the point of view of the reptilian brain: many people are focused on being the predator (getting what they want in order to survive and thrive, even if they walk over others to achieve their goals) and others are focused on avoiding being eaten by predators! Too often in such situations, the reptilian brain doesn't listen to the higher brain conscience that tells us what is right and what supports everyone's well-being.

If the reptilian brain is not at the service of our higher pre-frontal cortex, it quickly becomes a force of destruction for ourselves, our relationships and our society:

- Violence is an instinctual reptilian brain reaction in the face of what feels threatening even when there is no threat.

- Deception and competition in the workplace – whether in business, advertising, media or politics – is the name of the game for an uncontrolled reptilian brain, with its motto of eat or be eaten. Too often any sense of ethics is ignored in the ambitious climb to the top of the heap.

- Even sexual harassment emerges most often from this instinctual brain that wants what it wants right now, unconstrained by higher brain controls of right action.

The reptilian brain is aware only of the present moment of its own survival and self-gratification.

The limbic brain

The next brain to develop, in the second trimester in utero, is the limbic brain. Known as our emotional brain, it allows us to nurture our young and is the foundation for all our relationships. The limbic brain is also involved with memory, recording our emotional and survival experiences in the first three years of life. These experiences and our responses to them shape how we respond to events for the rest of our life.

Unlike the reptilian brain, the limbic brain is aware of both the present and the past. The limbic brain is more discriminating than the reptilian brain. It uses emotion – feelings – to evaluate relationships. The reptilian brain focuses on the outside world and our *survival* in that world, whereas the limbic brain focuses within on how we *feel* in response to the world.

The limbic brain handles our immune and hormonal systems, and our body's ability to heal itself. It also relates to how we learn. Because learning and memory are determined by the emotional state we are in when learning first takes place, the same emotional hormones – positive or negative – will continue to fire years later.

When our limbic brain loses its balance, our emotions highjack our higher thinking. When our negative emotional responses take control, we experience more pain and chaos.

The lower is integrated into the higher

Ideally, the earlier reptilian brain is meant to develop and then be integrated into the limbic or next higher brain. When this synthesis doesn't happen, the reptilian brain can take over the power of the limbic emotions:

- When threatened, we may fly into a rage or go into a violent reaction.

- We may go into a panic and our terror freezes all action.

- We may become obsessively jealous to the point that we are riddled with destructive feelings that can destroy our peace of mind, our health and our relationships.

Elephants charging

However, the reptilian brain definitely has appropriate responsibilities – giving us those knee-jerk reflex reactions when we are in any threatening or life/death survival situation. For instance, a friend from South Africa shared how he and his university friends went hiking on foot in the bush and unexpectedly walked over a hill into a herd of elephants. Upset by the surprise visit, one of the elephants began to charge. Without thinking, the students instinctively ran for their lives and shimmied up some trees. Only later did they discover, once the elephants had moved on, that the bark of the trees was covered in one-inch thorns, which had embedded in their skin without their even feeling them.

This is the reptilian brain at its best! But what happens when we need to think and consider various options or make a reasoned decision based on integrity and right action, or when we need to relate calmly? This is when our reptilian brain can disrupt our relationships, our career or hurt others through its reactive and harmful words and actions.

The neo-cortex

The third brain to develop is known as the neo-cortex – our verbal-intellectual brain. This brain begins to develop in the third trimester and is involved with language, thinking and the ability to consider all options objectively – rather than reacting instinctively or emotionally. It introduces the potential for creative imagination and calls us to expand our awareness and to keep learning.

Unlike the other two brains, our neo-cortex is aware of past, present and future.

The neo-cortex, from the front of the head to the back, occupies five times more skull space than the reptilian and limbic brains put together, and its hundred billion neurons (nerve cells) interact with all the other neurons to translate frequencies into our awareness.

The prefrontal cortex

The fourth brain is known as the prefrontal cortex or the prefrontal lobes. It is part of the neo-cortex and is found behind the ridge of our brow. In the East, the prefrontal lobes are associated with the third eye, the sixth energy reservoir or chakra. In the West, the prefrontals are associated with the human virtues of love, compassion, empathy, understanding, intelligence and the ability to reason, analyze, think and develop our creative imagination.

When the prefrontals regulate the limbic emotional responses, the reptilian instinctual reactions and even the analytical neo-cortex, we have the potential to become truly human and free of limitation – to transcend and create a new, more evolved reality.

Adrenaline arousal

Fear and anger, among other emotional responses, activate adrenaline, which keeps us locked in our reptilian survival brain and our emotionally discharging limbic brain. As long as we are in an adrenaline aroused state, very little clear thinking and loving communication are possible.

In *The Tao of Conversation*, author Michael Kahn mentions that in an emergency, what kills certain pilots is adrenaline. Fear shuts down the pilot's ability to think with reason and clarity (the prefrontal cortex). The pilot may have responded perfectly to numerous simulations of the same emergency, but in the real situation adrenaline takes over and lives are lost.

Healthy prefrontal activity

On the other hand, when the prefrontal lobes are active, it leads to clear thinking rather than to fight-flight adrenaline reactions. Pre-frontal activity provides the excitement of expanding our consciousness with new ideas, options and possibilities. And clear thinking controls the urge to discharge negative emotional reactions onto others.

The secret of the crack in the vase

The secret of the cracked vase is revealed when our out-of-sync mental and emotional states self-heal. This self-healing occurs when we access the higher brain awareness of our prefrontal lobes. Now we discover the purpose our wound leads us to. Now the light of our consciousness is capable of radiating love, compassion, integrity and understanding for the benefit of ourselves and others.

The REPATTERNING FOR RADIATING YOUR LIGHT that follows is a small beginning toward identifying the out-of-sync frequencies of our four brains, leading to the capacity to access the light of consciousness from our prefrontal cortex.

The young man whose leg was amputated transcended the control his lower reptilian and limbic brains had over his higher brain consciousness. When he integrated these two lower brains into the higher neo-cortex and prefrontal cortex, he discovered his light and purpose and was able to help others regain their true sense of self, as he himself had done.

Protecting ourselves from negative reactions

There is only one way to protect ourselves from negative reactions and that is by bringing our reptilian and limbic brains into the service of our higher prefrontal awareness. Only in this way can we project the higher mind qualities of love, understanding, empathy and non-judgment rather than lower mind reactiveness.

As our frequencies come into sync with what is positive or coherent, we are freed of all judgments concerning others' actions. After all, negative actions simply reflect out-of-sync frequencies that need to self-heal by returning to their natural in-sync state of coherence.

As we saw in the story of the cracked vase, when we come from love and a sense of service, positive change automatically begins to happen.

For example, three Resonance Repatterning practitioners from Mexico were invited to visit an island prison thirteen hours by boat from the mainland of Mexico. The practitioners volunteered to spend seven days doing group and individual Resonance Repatterning sessions.

Even after such a short visit, the head of the prison said he could see changes in the prisoners' behavior. He said they were motivated by the love they experienced in their one-hour Repatterning sessions.

Loving actions help people reconnect to the light within themselves. Then positive change begins to happen naturally, effortlessly for both the giver and the receiver.

In our essence there is nothing but love and positivity – the light of consciousness. We all yearn to access this part of ourselves. On some level we are all in a prison of our own making, longing for freedom from our lower tendencies – our un-integrated reptilian and limbic brains.

Each one of us has cracks in the vase of who we are and how we behave. But with love and compassion we begin to see beyond these cracks of anger, fear, jealousy, pain, hate, violence and abuse, to the light within. And one day, by doing our own inner work, the pain we experience and the suffering we impose on ourselves and others can become the opening that allows our light to shine through.

The greatest protection and healing in the world is unconditional love. This highest of all frequencies is accessed through stilling our mind in meditation. And we support this process by resonating with what is positive and life-giving and by doing the inner work of bringing our lower brains into the service of our higher prefrontal cortex.

When a person's vase is severely cracked, he or she needs compassion, a loving presence, non-judgment and a vision of the transformation that is possible. For example, in Japan when a valuable bowl is broken, it is put back together by filling in the cracks with gold: a thing of beauty is created out of what was once broken. And it is the same with us.

The purpose of Resonance Repatterning is to support the kind of integration that makes it possible to manifest the higher qualities of the human spirit, no matter what the cracked circumstances of our life may be.

FURTHER READING

Michael Kahn. *The Tao of Conversation.* Oakland, CA: New Harbinger Publications, 1995.

Joseph Chilton Pierce. *The Biology of Transcendence.* Rochester, VT: Park Street Press, 2002.

Rachel Naomi Remen, M.D. *Kitchen Table Wisdom.* New York, NY: Riverhead Books, 1996.

1.

REPATTERNING FOR RADIATING YOUR LIGHT

REPATTERNING FOR
RADIATING YOUR LIGHT

A. Read or tell the story of the crack in the vase *p.5*
Ask, "What does this story mean for you?"
*[**cr**]with "I (*name the positive meaning*)" (*will be off/umb off*).

B. Name the present upset
Do {a–b} in sequence.

a. *Ask,* "What is your wound, your place of suffering, and who is involved?"
*[**cr**] with, "I am in pain because (*name the suffering*)" (*will be on/umb on because at this time client resonates with the out-of-sync frequencies causing the pain, the wound*).

Deeper understanding in relation to the four brains
Explain: A negative experience or wound of any sort – whether outside yourself or in your own thoughts and feelings – tends to shift your energy from your higher prefrontal cortex behind your brow, to your lower reptilian survival brain and your limbic emotional brain. This shift locks your higher brain into the service or control of your lower and emotionally reactive survival brains. As a result, understanding, clear thinking, joy and harmonious communication may not feel available to you.

b. Have client draw a picture of themselves, the suffering, the wound.
*[**cr**] (will be on/umb on).*

C. Name the reptilian and limbic brain responses
Do {a–f} in sequence.

a. *[**cr**] with "I react in an instinctual fight-flight way that doesn't help me or (*name person/others*)" (*will be on/umb on*).

b. *[**cr**] with "My emotions take control of my higher brain thinking and I experience pain and chaos in my thinking" (*will be on/umb on*).

c. *Ask*, "What is most threatening for you about this situation?"
*[cr] with "I feel threatened in case (*name threat*)" *(will be on/umb on because at this time client resonates with **this reptilian brain threat**).*

d. *Ask*, "What are you afraid of?"
*[cr] with "I am afraid (*name fear*)" *(will be on/umb on because client resonates with **this limbic brain fear and reptilian brain 'flight' response**).*

e. *Ask*, "What are you angry about in this situation?"
*[cr] with "I am angry that (*name anger*)" *(will be on/umb on because client resonates with **this limbic brain anger and reptilian brain 'fight' response**).*

f. *Ask*, "What are you jealous of that (*name person/others*) has and you don't have?"
*[cr] with "I feel (weak • inadequate • inferior • unattractive) because (*name what others have that client does not have*)" *(will be on/umb on because client resonates with **this limbic brain emotional response**).*

D. Name the earlier experience being reactivated
Do {a–e} in sequence.
a. *Ask*, "What earlier experience does your present pain remind you of?"
*[cr] with the past experience as though it is present *(will be on/umb on because client resonates with this earlier reptilian-limbic brain threat as though it is still present).*

b. *Ask*, "What do you imagine you needed back then?"
*[cr] with "I have/am (*name the need*)" *(will be off/umb off because, based on the earlier experience, client is unable to resonate with what he/she needs in the present).*

c. *Ask*, "How do you imagine you felt in that earlier experience?"
*[cr] with "I continue to feel (*name the feeling*) in the present" *(will be on/umb on because client still resonates with this painful feeling from the past).*

d. *Ask*, "What do you imagine you believed about yourself/others as a result of that past difficult experience?"
*[**cr**] *(will be on/umb on because client still resonates with this negative belief about him/herself)*.

e. *Ask*, "What do you want instead of that experience?"
Explain: Everything is in the mind. The experience is over, yet you still carry its resonance with you as though it is still present – and this automatically activates your two lower brains whenever you are triggered in the present. When you say what you want instead, and resonate with it, it creates new neural connections with your higher brain.

*[**cr**] *(will be off/umb off because client does not resonate with new neural connections for this higher-brain vision of what is possible)*.

E. New possibility for fear
Ask, "Where do you imagine your fear is pointing you to? Your fear wants you to empower yourself and (*name person/others*) in a positive way. How can you do this?"
*[**cr**] *(will be off/umb off)*.

F. New possibility for anger
Ask, "Where do you imagine your anger is pointing you to? What is a new positive vision for your life that would give you a sense of hope?"
*[**cr**] *(will be off/umb off)*.

G. New possibility for jealousy
Ask, "Where do you imagine your jealousy (weakness or inadequacy) is pointing you to? What is unique about you? What are your strengths?"
*[**cr**] *(will be off/umb off)*.

H. Avoiding reactivating the limbic and reptilian survival brain
(**mcs**) {a–h} for the one(s) needed.
*[**cr**] *(will be off/umb off)*.
a. I avoid focusing on who is right and who is wrong.

b. I avoid (arguing • reacting with anger) and I connect to my higher understanding and wisdom.

c. (I stop projecting what I think (*name person*) is feeling or needing • I stop projecting negative thoughts).

d. I avoid (labeling • criticizing • blaming • gossiping about) (*name person*).

e. I avoid getting defensive in response to (*name person*)'s negative feelings about me.

f. I avoid invalidating (*name person*) and making him/her wrong.

g. I avoid justifying my actions and feelings.

h. I stop repetitively thinking about upsets and allowing my thoughts to go round in circles endlessly.

I. Prefrontal qualities needed

(**mcs**) {1–11} for the primary one needed in relation to the present upset.
*[**cr**] (*will be off/umb off*).

1. I control my impulse to react (negatively • non-coherently) in the moment.
2. I stay focused on what is most important.
3. I am peaceful.
4. I listen with empathy.
5. I think clearly.
6. I listen, free of needing to interrupt.
7. I make good decisions (that benefit all concerned • that are based on what is right).
8. I listen to my conscience.
9. I am in control of my emotions.
10. I share my insight as a way to re-establish harmony.
11. I set goals and make plans for achieving them.

J. Bringing the lower brains into sync with the prefrontal cortex by client sharing his/her point of view

Do {a–c} in sequence.

Explain: When our reptilian and limbic brains are controlled by, or in the service of the higher prefrontal cortex, we experience life from a different point of view – with a sense of purpose, seeing new options and wanting to share our experiences to benefit others. This possibility starts when we keep the lines of communication open by listening and openly exploring both points of view, and feeling heard, understood and acknowledged. In {a–c} below we are not checking resonance with the feeling, but with communicating the feeling free of reaction.

a. Communicate your upset feelings honestly and lovingly in response to (*person's actions*). (Practitioner represents person involved throughout this communication process).

Practitioner states, "I'm checking your resonance with **communicating** your feelings to (*name person*)":

*[**cr**] with "I feel (*name the upset feeling*) when you (*name what the person does that makes you feel upset*)" (will be off/umb off because client doesn't yet resonate with **communicating** his/her feelings directly and lovingly to the person involved, free of blame and criticism).*

b. *Ask,* "What do you need from (*name person*)?"
Practitioner says, "I'm checking your resonance with **communicating** your need to (*name person*)":

*[**cr**] with, "What would make a difference for me is (*name the need*)" (will be off/umb off because client doesn't resonate at this time with having needs and **communicating** them in a way that they are heard by the person involved).*

c. *Explain:* It is important that you feel heard and acknowledged with empathy – even if (*name person*) thinks and feels differently from you.

*[**cr**] with "I don't feel heard and understood by you (*name person*), I feel disconnected from you and unable to go into **right action with self-confidence**" (will be on/umb on because client resonates at this time with being affected by (name upset person)'s reactions, rather than client being confident in his/her prefrontal decision based on his/her conscience of what is right at this time).*

K. **Bringing the lower brains into sync with the prefrontal cortex by client understanding (*name person*)'s point of view**

Do {a–c} in sequence.

Explain: To activate your prefrontal cortex, you need to move beyond right/wrong, win/lose arguments either in your own mind or with the person involved.

You will also need to transcend being stuck in your own defensive position.

What is important is to give your full attention to each other's point of view; to hear and acknowledge the other person's needs; and to acknowledge your own feelings and needs, which are different from the other person's.

Exploring both points of view equally, without arguing or defending your truth, usually leads to a solution that works for those involved, or leads to constructive action that allows your light to shine through the crack in your vase, even though the differences may continue to exist.

As you do this, your reptilian survival brain and limbic emotional brains are now in the service of your higher prefrontal cortex, which always leads to a sense of relief and a feeling of rightness when you follow your conscience, no matter how hard it may be for you to initiate the action you feel is right.

a. *Ask,* "What do you imagine (*name person*) is feeling in this situation?" Practitioner says, "I'm checking your resonance with **listening** to (*name person*)'s feelings and responding with empathy and understanding":

*[**cr**] with "(*Name person*) **shares his/her feelings** with me that (*name feelings*) and I listen with empathy and understanding" (will be off/umb off because client doesn't yet resonate with listening free of reptilian and limbic-brain reactiveness and with prefrontal understanding).*

b. *Ask,* "What do you imagine (*name person*) truly **needs**?" Practitioner says, "I'm checking your resonance with **listening** to (*name person*)'s needs with empathy and understanding":

*[cr]with "(*Name person*) **shares with me that he/she needs** (*name the need*) and I listen with empathy and understanding" (*will be off/umb off*).

c. *Explain:* It is important that (*name person*) feels heard and acknowledged by you with empathy, even if you think and feel differently from him/her.

*[cr] with, "When I hear and understand (*name person*), he/she feels connected to me and able to go into right action with self-confidence" (*will be off/umb off because client doesn't resonate with this listening and understanding*).

L. Identify how *client* wants to radiate his/her light
Explain: If this pain is the crack in your vase, it is also the opening that will allow your light to shine through.

Ask, "How can you use this suffering with (*name person*) in a positive way? What do you imagine your pain wants you to learn and do?"
*[cr] (*will be off/umb off because client doesn't resonate at this time with the opening, growth and learning that he/she is being challenged to initiate*).

M. Identify the Energizing Option needed for the prefrontal cortex to effortlessly modulate all lower brain functioning
(**mcs**) for the Energizing Option from the SPIRAL UP! book that is needed for shifting the resonance patterns identified in this Repatterning.

If you are a Resonance Repatterning practitioner, you can then recheck the *[cr] statements to confirm the change in resonance.

N. Look at the original picture
Ask, "Do you want to change it in any way or draw another picture?"

HOW TO USE THE REPATTERNING FOR RADIATING YOUR LIGHT IN YOUR DAILY LIFE
EVEN IF YOU HAVE NOT YET ATTENDED A RESONANCE REPATTERNING SEMINAR

- Whenever you feel upset or are about to react, take **a two-second pause.** Be aware that when you refuse to indulge your reptilian and limbic brain reactions, which are based on past experiences, those old neural pathways begin to atrophy from lack of use.

- Consciously create a new neural pathway with your prefrontal cortex by staying focused on the positive, thinking clearly and taking your time to come to a decision based on what your conscience determines is right action.

- When upset and feeling there is no light shining through the crack in your vase, try doing even one or two of the letters in this **Repatterning** plus an Energizing Option to change your resonance.

- If the person involved is open, read through this **Repatterning** together.

- This **Repatterning** is worth returning to whenever you feel yourself going into your non-coherent reptilian and limbic brain reactions and you want to bring your higher brain prefrontal cortex into the picture.

RR SESSIONS: If you would like to receive the complete Repatterning with a professional Resonance Repatterning Practitioner, in person or over the phone, go to ResonanceRepatterning.net > Sessions for RR Institute Practitioners worldwide who have listed themselves on the RRI website.

RR SEMINARS: If you would like to attend Resonance Repatterning seminars in person or online, so you can use RR effectively on yourself and/or others, go to ResonanceRepatterning.net > Seminars for the list of teachers endorsed by the Resonance Repatterning Institute to teach.

2. ANYTHING IS POSSIBLE

Life is a daring adventure or nothing.
Helen Keller

Optimism is true moral courage.
Sir Ernest Shackleton

There is something exciting about secrets: something that is only known to a few – a mystery.

Secrets comes from the Latin to 'sift', and in this chapter we'll be sifting what makes **anything possible** – the five secrets.

All extraordinary people who do amazing things in their life put these five secrets into practice.

Is it possible for us to do the same? I think so.

- First we need to know what the five secrets are.

- Then we need to resonate with them.

- And finally we hardwire them in our brain by living them – whether in our spiritual practice, family life, our creative expressions and hobbies, or in our work and what we want to contribute to the world. If you are a student, you can even apply these five secrets to your studies.

We are all a part of the infinite field of vibrating frequencies talked about in quantum physics. When we resonate with the positive, it automatically amplifies and attracts what is positive, energizing and life-giving from this infinite field of vibrating frequencies.

Before looking at the five secrets, I'd like to share a story with you about a man who epitomizes all five of them – a man who resonated with the positive and attracted the positive from the infinite field of vibrating frequencies in spite of life-defying obstacles.

STORY OF SIR ERNEST SHACKLETON

The following true story is about Sir Ernest Shackleton – the man who failed to reach the South Pole, but whose achievement boggles the imagination. What he did has been called one of history's greatest epics of survival.

Shackleton lived the five secrets that made this epic possible.

In 1914 just as World War 1 was breaking out, Shackleton and twenty-seven explorers, sailors, scientists, doctors and a photographer set sail for Antarctica from the whaling station on South Georgia Island – roughly on the same parallel with the southernmost tip of South America, thousands of miles to the east of it. Their goal was to be dropped off on Antarctica and be the first to cross this frozen continent on foot.

After one month of sailing south and just eighty-five miles from their landing base, their small sailing ship, the *Endurance,* became stuck in pack ice and began to drift with the ice flows northwards, away from their destination.

In below zero temperatures, gale-force winds and six months of darkness, the ship drifted until, ten months after leaving the island of South Georgia, it was crushed in the pack ice – broken into matchsticks.

The men set up camp on the ice flow, sleeping on ground sheets that weren't waterproof, living in linen tents that were so thin the moon could be seen through them, and sleeping in wet sleeping bags that froze into iron sheets. They had salvaged food supplies that would last about three months and they had three small open boats.

The ice flows were unstable, cracking open and closing up, sometimes only a few feet of ice between them and the sea beneath. Finally they floated towards Elephant Island eight hundred miles southwest of the whaling station on South Georgia Island where their journey south had started.

Shackleton decided the time had come to leave the disintegrating pack ice, take to their three small open boats and face the most dangerous part of their journey. They now had to keep to the open water and escape being crushed whenever two large masses of pack ice clamped together.

Seasick, sleepless, exposed to constant rain and snow squalls, soaked through in minus seven degree temperatures, they attempted to make a run for Elephant Island in gale force winds that blew surging waves into their boats.

After two days and nights without water or hot food, with swollen lips, boils and dysentery, they now faced the precipitous coastline of Elephant Island. They had spent seven days in open boats on the south Atlantic, six months drifting on ice flows with inadequate clothing, shelter and food, and it had been sixteen months since they had set foot on land. Somehow they got through an opening in the reef. Exhausted, they slept in their wet sleeping bags in a blizzard that ripped the largest tent to ribbons.

The day after their arrival on this narrow spit of land beneath towering cliffs, Shackleton announced another momentous decision – that six of them would sail in the twenty-two foot open boat for the whaling station on South Georgia Island, eight hundred miles to the east, across the most formidable ocean on the planet.

They knew they would be sailing through the notorious Cape Horn rollers, measuring from trough to crest as much as sixty feet in height, with winds at eighty miles an hour, or more.

The small group that Shackleton had selected spent the next sixteen days on this epic journey: an intense gale that lasted for days, soaked every three to four minutes day and night, having to chip ice from the boat so it wouldn't sink under the extra weight.

With two of the men close to death and two days without any fresh water, they finally neared South Georgia Island, only to face jagged reefs spouting water forty feet into the air. They waited out the night in the hail, sleet and snow in a hurricane that drove them toward the jagged coast. The small boat sheered away from the cliffs and suddenly the hurricane, which they had fought for nine hours, subsided.

The next day was spent trying to gain entry through a gap in the jagged reef line. Finally, after the fifth attempt, they made it through. Only later would they learn that a 500-ton steamer was wrecked in the same hurricane they had just weathered. And years later they would learn that their voyage was ranked as one of the greatest boat journeys ever made.

But their journey was far from over. After four days of waiting out bad weather, Shackleton decided that with their level of exhaustion and the jagged coastline, it was too dangerous to try to reach the whaling station by boat. He announced that three of them would cross the unnamed glaciers and unmapped snow-covered mountain range on foot – and would come back by boat for the remaining three men.

With three days' minimal provisions and no sleeping bags, Shackleton and two other men began their ascent across the mountains that no one had ever ventured through. They traveled for thirty-six hours without rest. Exhausted, their filthy clothes in tatters, their bearded faces black with blubber smoke, they finally arrived at the small whaling station on the other side of the mountains.

Later an old Norwegian whaler described the meeting when they arrived at the station manager's home: "Manager say: 'Who the hell are you?' and terrible bearded man in the centre of the three say very quietly: 'My name is Shackleton.' Me – I turn away and weep."

Finally they had their first hot baths, clean dry clothes and plentiful food in almost two years. They quickly picked up the other three men waiting on the far side of South Georgia Island. But with WWI raging in Europe, it took four months and four different attempts before they managed to get back to Elephant Island through the ice flows to save the twenty-two men they had left there. Shackleton's vision was accomplished: every life was saved and each man made it safely home.

Amazing and inspiring as this story is, we may wonder what relevance his epic has for us, right now in present time. The lessons of this story are timeless. Like all great achievements, Shackleton's extraordinary leadership teaches us about the five secrets, which prove that anything is possible – and that each one of us can resonate with them and apply them in our own lives.

Secret #1: Vision

The first secret is to have a vision. Shackleton had one great vision that he held onto through every horrendous challenge he and his crew faced, and which determined every decision he made: to bring each man home alive.

If we want to achieve our own greatness, we need to ask ourself: What is the vision that brings purpose to my life, that I can live with passion and that determines every decision I make?"

A true vision is what inspires us and brings meaning and purpose to our life. It is something we want to live every day for the rest of our life – something we are deeply passionate about. It is something that directly or indirectly helps others.

A true vision it is not about money or security or power or material well-being or fame and name. These are desires and goals. A true vision may involve the *opposite* of these desires: *no* money, security, power, well-being, fame or name!

Victor Frankl, who wrote about his experience in a Nazi concentration camp, said that those who had a sense of meaning were often the ones who survived – even though they weren't necessarily the strongest or healthiest. Without meaning or vision, even stronger healthier people couldn't make it through.

So we need to remind ourselves every day, "What is my vision? What brings purpose to my life?" It is this vision that motivates us in our life.

Secret #2: Acceptance free of resistance

The second secret is to accept what is, free of resistance. Those who powerfully transcend great challenges always accept the reality of what is. They don't waste their energy fighting, resisting or complaining about the reality of what is. They accept and go into action.

- Shackleton lived in the present moment.

- He accepted what is.

- He constantly moved into action towards his vision.

Complaining, blaming, criticizing, gossiping, talking about how hard things are, achieves nothing. This negative attitude depletes our energy and makes coherent action impossible.

Secret #3: Let go of regrets

The third secret each one of us needs to resonate with is to let go of regrets. The men of The *Endurance* said that Shackleton never gave in to regrets. Standing on the frozen ice flow and watching his ship being crushed to matchsticks – a moment he was unable to write about in his diary – he let go of the pain, free of regret. No what if.

He spent no time wishing the past could have been different. He kept his eyes and thoughts on the present moment and on the vision he was determined to achieve – that each person there would survive and make it home.

This secret is more important than we realize. How many of us do small daily irritating actions that we wish we hadn't done or get irritated at actions we wish we didn't have to do? How many of us then make the situation worse by wasting our energy regretting our thoughts and actions!

Instead, if we put Secret #3 into action, we recognize what is, we accept that negative thoughts and actions will never take us closer to realizing our vision, so we let go of regrets, pick ourselves up and get to work once more moving towards our vision.

Secret #4: Hope and optimism

The fourth secret is to maintain hope and optimism. The crew of the *Endurance* said that Shackleton was totally optimistic. No matter what happened, he maintained his sense of hope. As he himself said, "Optimism is true moral courage."

He upheld the morale of his men through almost two years of unsurpassed challenge through his optimistic and hopeful attitude. Again, by resonating constantly with hope and optimism in our own life, we can avoid the hopelessness and negativity that weaken our immune system and deplete our energy reserves. Optimism helps us cross the sea of our own challenges.

Secret #5: Persevering action

The fifth secret is persevering action – never giving up until we achieve our vision. Walt Disney is an example of persevering action: he went bankrupt four times before he finally became successful.

This secret is about keeping on going no matter what – until our last breath. Persevering action is what keeps us going in the face of every apparent failure. If Shackleton had given up, all lives would have been lost.

How many of us become hopeless and give up in the face of obstacles or apparent failure, or when our dreams don't materialize in the way we want them to, or *when* we want them to?

STORY OF A VISION TO ERADICATE WORLDWIDE POVERTY

Muhammad Yunus had a vision to eradicate worldwide poverty through microcredit to the poorest of the poor. In following his vision, he faced one obstacle after another. In the beginning one of his big hurdles was persuading the poverty-stricken women of Bangladesh, who earn one or two cents a day, to accept his microloans of $5 or less. Day after day he would return to the village, talk to the women, win their confidence, until finally a few had the courage to break the social rules that mired them in submission and poverty. Forty-two families finally accepted his very first loan, a total of $27. Now thirty years later, the Grameen bank he founded has lent $6 billion to nearly seven million poor people, 97% of whom are women!

Anything is possible when you radiate the light of your vision. As Yunus writes, "We achieve what we want to achieve. If we are not achieving something, it is because we have not put our minds to it. We create what we want." Here is a man who lives the five secrets: vision; accepting what is; letting go of regrets about what doesn't work; maintaining his optimism in the face of every challenge; and persevering through obstacles that are beyond our imagination.

Thinking of ourselves in the same light as people like Ernest Shackleton and Muhammad Yunus seems laughable. But the five secrets they lived are not so impossible. Once we resonate with the five secrets and put them into action in small ways in our daily life, we become energized by them. Our life takes on a bigger meaning. We experience for ourselves that living these five secrets gives us access to the field of limitless possibilities for a life where we make a difference, not only to ourselves, but to all those we touch. The power of one starts with each person. It can be us.

FURTHER READING

Caroline Alexander. *The Endurance: Shackleton's Legendary Antarctic Expedition.* New York, NY: Alfred A. Knopf, 2006.

Muhammad Yunus. *Banker to the Poor.* NY: PublicAffairs, 1999.

Arthur Samuel Joseph. *Vocal Power: Harnessing the Power Within.* San Diego, CA: Jodere Group, 2003.

2.

ANYTHING IS POSSIBLE REPATTERNING

ANYTHING IS POSSIBLE REPATTERNING

This Repatterning is helpful for someone who has a vision for who they want to be or what they want to do and achieve, but is feeling despondent in the face of obstacles and failures.

A. Read or tell the story about Sir Ernest Shackleton *p.28*
Ask, "What does this story mean for you?" *[cr] with "I (*name the positive meaning*)" (*will be off/umb off*).

B. Identify the challenge
Ask, "What challenge are you facing where you are failing in your efforts to realize your vision or you are not getting the results you want from your efforts?"
*[cr] (*will be on/umb on because client resonates with not being able to successfully face the challenge*).

C. Identify the four aspects of failed effort
Do {a–d} in sequence.
a. *Ask,* "How do you feel when you fail in your efforts or don't get the results you want from your efforts?"
  *[cr] (*will be on/umb on because client resonates with the limbic brain feelings of failure. The limbic brain is activated by the negative feeling stress response rather than by positive feeling responses*).

b. *Ask,* "What do you regret? Name any regret."
  *[cr] with "I am holding on to my regret that (*name regrets*) and this keeps me stuck in the past rather than living my vision in the present" (*will be on/umb on because as long as client resonates with regrets, he/she is living in the past*).

c. *[cr] with "(I feel hopeless • I lose my optimism • I feel like giving up)" (*will be on/umb on*).

d. *[**cr**] with "In the face of my failed actions (I give up • I stop persevering toward my goal through right action • I keep repeating actions that don't take me towards my goal • I don't use my willpower to get myself back on track through right actions)" *(will be on/umb on).*

D. Secret #1 – Identify the vision needed
Understanding Vision

Do {a–b} in sequence.

a. Read or tell the story of **A vision to eradicate worlwide poverty** *p.34* *Ask,* "What does this story mean for you?" *[**cr**] with "I *(name the positive meaning)*" *(will be off/umb off).*

b. *Ask,* "What is your life vision – a vision you want to live for the rest of your life, that inspires you, brings a sense of meaning to you, that you feel passionate about and that determines every decision you make?" *[**cr**] (will be off/umb off because client doesn't resonate with the responsibility of such a vision).*

Explain: Greatness and achieving great things in your life begins with a vision that inspires you. A vision is not just an action or goal or doing something that gives you pleasure.

A vision is *big*! It is demanding, challenging! It is also your lifeline – something you don't want to live without.

Having a vision and maintaining it through thick and thin is part of your growth and inner evolution. Meeting the challenges of your vision strengthens you and makes you develop as a human being.

Each action aligned to your vision makes you receptive, even in the smallest way, to the field of limitless possibilities talked about in new physics and ancient wisdom traditions. The field of limitless possibilities responds to a coherent vision, even while it demands constant growth by overcoming all inner and outer obstacles that arise on the way.

E. Secret #2 – Accept what is
Understanding Accept what is
Explain: If you don't accept what is happening to you, the resistance causes constriction and tension in your body, mind and feelings, which results in more stress, upset or pain and creates unnecessary obstacles to the achievement of your vision.

Acceptance represents a highly vibrating coherent frequency. When you resonate with accepting what is happening to you free of all resistance, you tune in to this highly vibrating frequency, which helps you transcend the difficulties or pain you are passing through. The sword wound is transformed into a pinprick.

The high state of coherence that acceptance brings can, even by itself, have what appears to be miraculous benefits – whether self-healing or the strength to face the challenges you are going through with inner calm.

Acceptance does not mean you are passive or that you give up. Acceptance always involves assertive right action. It is said that people who survive extreme situations – for example, airplane crashes in remote mountain areas – are those who accept the reality of what is and then go into unhesitating action.

When you refuse to accept the reality of what is (often going into complaints, blame, upset or hopelessness), it creates stress. Stress creates a non-coherent chaotic frequency field that makes unhesitating action, self-healing or survival difficult or impossible. In response to daily upsets or stress, if you repeat "I accept (*name the issue*) free of all resistance," even without changing your resonance, you'll notice something positive begins to happen.

Do {a–b} in sequence.
a. *Ask,* "What are you having trouble accepting in terms of (*name the challenge {B}*) and (*name the vision {D}*)?"
   *[**cr**] with, "I accept (*name what client listed in {B}*) free of all resistance and I go into unhesitating action to get back on track with my vision of

(name vision {D})" *(will be off/umb off because client doesn't resonate with accepting what is and going into unhesitating action to get back on track).*

b. *Explain*: Whenever we have trouble accepting anything, we know a negative belief is involved. A belief is a thought we take to be true – and a negative belief blocks the realization of our vision.

Ask, "What do you imagine your negative belief is concerning *(name the challenge)* and *(name the vision)*?"
*[**cr**] *(will be on/umb on because client resonates with this negative belief).*

F.   Secret #3 – Identify the regrets involved
Understanding Regrets
Explain: We spend a lot of time and energy regretting what we've done or said, or what we have not done or said, and we also waste energy thinking about and regretting the outcomes we want but have not achieved.

Regrets take energy and spiral us down to a depleted state of despondency, hopelessness and even depression. In such a state, our mind reacts and we do actions that take us away from our vision rather than towards it – and these actions lead to further regrets.

If we want to achieve our vision, we need to be receptive to the higher learning in every regret and then let go of the regret itself and move on. Every time we resonate with the learning of any regret we have, we will automatically go into some kind of positive action towards our vision.

Do {a–b} in sequence.
a. *Ask,* "What do you regret in relation to *(name the challenging situation)* and *(name the vision)*?"
*[**cr**] with, "I let go of my regret that *(name the regrets)"* *(will be off/umb off because client doesn't resonate with **letting go** of the regrets).*

b. *Ask,* "What can you learn from your regret(s) *{C b}*?"
*[**cr**] with the learning, leaving out "I learn" or "I can" *(will be off/umb off because client doesn't resonate with the learning).*

G. Secret #4 – Hope, optimism and gratitude
Understanding Hope, optimism and gratitude
Ask, "What is there to feel hopeful and optimistic about and what are you grateful for?"
*[**cr**] with, "I feel hopeful and optimistic that *(name the hope and optimism)* and I feel grateful for *(name the gratitude)*" *(will be off/umb off).*

Explain: Hope, optimism and gratitude are high-frequency qualities that energize you and make it possible for you to maintain and work towards your vision. When you lose hope, you also lose all motivation to keep going: you give up and become despondent. You may spend the rest of your life grieving a lost dream. You may feel that life is not worth living.

Hope, optimism and gratitude keep you going towards achieving your vision:

- They boost your immune system.

- They keep you alive and healthy.

- They motivate you to keep going, no matter what the obstacles.

- They give you faith.

- They keep you growing towards your vision.

- They make you receptive to the limitless field of energy, which makes all things possible.

H. Secret #5 – Persevering action

Understanding Perseverance *Read the following slowly and out loud*

Manifesting positive thoughts, intentions and our vision in the physical creation is difficult to say the least. It takes work and commitment and unbelievable perseverance. Seemingly insurmountable challenges may beset our path. Often it may feel easier to give in to our mind's desire to give up, rather than overcome the obstacles we are facing.

In the final leg of Shackleton's journey, they spent thirty-six hours climbing over unmapped mountains and glaciers to get to the whaling station on the other side of South Georgia island. Shackleton and his two companions – in a state of exhaustion and with no food, water or shelter – lay down to rest in the snow. Shackleton knew that if all three of them slept, they would never wake up. So he forced himself to stand up and stay awake. After five minutes he woke up the two men, telling them they had slept for half an hour. Shackleton lived his vision every second. His vision to bring every man home alive determined every decision he made.

To achieve our vision, we will have to face the resistance of our mind, emotions and body because they want the easy way – the way of least resistance.

But we need to appreciate that there is also power in resistance: an airplane cannot land when there is not enough resistance in the air – when the temperature rises about 120 degrees fahrenheit, for instance. When a bird's wings meet the resistance of air, it flies; when a fish's fins meet the resistance of water, it swims; when our feet meet the resistance of the ground, we dance, jump and run. When Shackleton resisted his need to sleep, he was empowered and saved the lives of his whole crew.

But our pleasure-loving mind and emotions want things to be easy, enjoyable and free of resistance. We need to accept that working towards our vision requires that we face resistance – obstacles and problems. And we need resistance if we want to fly.

By successfully handling resistance, great things are achieved: we gain the strength and capacity to achieve the very thing we most want – the realization of our vision.

Each obstacle we meet makes us stronger and more capable of handling the *next* obstacle, until finally we attain our vision. At the very least we will live a visionary and heroic life trying – and that's all that counts.

The vision we have changes us, molds us and ennobles us with its demand that we rise above any weakness that comes between us and our vision. Athletes, dancers and musicians with the vision to reach the top – to be the best they can be in their chosen art form – constantly face the hard daily work, the exhaustion and the intense climb towards perfection. The finished result is beautiful.

So it is with us. With each daily resistance we meet – by living the five secrets of vision, acceptance, letting go of regrets, maintaining our hope, optimism and gratitude, and continuing with persevering action – we too become beautiful: the beauty of living at a higher frequency, which directly or indirectly inspires others to find and live their vision.

Do {a–d} in sequence.
a. **Persevering actions**
    Ask, "What persevering actions do you need to take to realize your vision?"
    *[**cr**] (will be off/umb off).

b. **Doing whatever it takes**
    Write down, "I persevere toward (*name the vision {D}*) with hope and optimism and with gratitude at every step. I do whatever it takes in the face of all apparent failures."
    *[**cr**] (will be off/umb off).

c. **The discipline needed**
    Ask, "What discipline do you need to integrate into your life that will help you?"
    *[**cr**] with "I have the discipline to (*name the actions*)" (will be off/umb off).

d. **Containment of emotional reactions and mental restlessness**
    Write down, "When meeting resistance to my vision, I contain (my emotional-mental restlessness • the urge to do actions that don't support my vision • the temptation to justify doing actions that I know don't support the realization of my vision) and I go into right action.
    *[**cr**] (will be off/umb off).*

I. The Energizing Option of eight acupuncture points without needles

The following Energizing Option – eight acupuncture points to balance your meridians without needles – aims to support you as you meet your challenges on the way to achieving your vision.

If you have studied Resonance Repatterning, you can muscle check which of these points is needed and for the details of whether to use the ColorYourWorld Torch, Tuning Forks or an essential oil on the points.

For non-Resonance Repatterning people, you may use a finger contact on one or more of these points.
See ResonanceRepatterning.net > Home Study Course for Inner Cultivation

* **Earth Element, Stomach Meridian**: This point is about two inches below the knee crease on the outer edge of the leg. Slide your finger into the muscles towards your shin bone and see if you can feel the point.

    This point is called Leg Three Miles. The ancient Chinese Acupuncturists believed that it supports longevity and revitalizes your energy. It is wonderful to use this point when you need endurance, stamina, stability and especially when you are worried about harvesting positive results from what you have done, or feel there will be no harvest for the work you have put in. This point will help strengthen your resolve to keep moving forward, keeping you grounded and energized for your onward journey.

* **Metal Element, Lung Meridian**: The point is under the clavicle where it meets the shoulder.

This point is called Cloud Gate. It is uplifting, helping you reconnect to the Divine within yourself, to see through the clouds of difficulties, to have faith that the sun is still shining beyond the clouds.

- **Water Element, Bladder Meridian:** The point is on either side of your spine at the top of your neck, just under the ridge of your skull bone, on the large trapesius neck muscle. Your two fingers will be about an inch away from the spine, one on each side.

   This point is called Heavenly Pillar. It gives you the strength, power, calmness and energy to handle the resistance of your challenges and gives you the inner strength to keep reaching for your vision free of fear.

- **Wood Element, Liver Meridian:** The point underneath the middle of the ribs on both sides.

   This point is called Gate of Hope. It gives you the hope, optimism and vision to handle your stress with positive action, coherent plans and decisions that are aligned with your vision.

- **Fire Element, Heart Protector Meridian:** With the palm facing up, the point is found on the middle of the wrist in the hollow that you can feel when you flex your hand towards you.

   This point is called Great Mound – The burial ground for emperors – a place of great power. Great Mound gives you a renewed sense of confidence, safety, trust and love when you are feeling vulnerable or when you need to call on the strength of your generational history for support and vision.

- **Fire Element, Triple Heater Meridian:** With your arm bent and the palm facing the shoulder, this point is about an inch above the tip of the elbow on the back of the upper arm.

   This point is called Heavenly Well. It strengthens the mind and spirit by helping you recharge yourself through connection to the divine – an inexhaustible well that has only good to bring.

- **Fire Element, Heart Meridian**: This point is at your armpits, behind the tendon – children like to place their thumbs on these points!

  This point is called Utmost Source. It is a wonderful point to use when there is chaos, confusion, agitation or when you no longer feel oriented towards your vision. Do this point when you need to reconnect deeply to the ultimate source of love, compassion and consciousness within yourself.

- **Fire Element, Small Intestine Meridian:** This point is on the outer edge of the little finger just above the notch of the base joint of the little finger.

  This point is called Forward Valley. It gives you the drive and perseverance to transform life's problems into challenging adventures. It empowers you to sort out what is rich and to act on what enriches your life. It helps you move forward fearlessly and with willpower when you have much to sort out, helping you conserve your energy by doing what is important, and leaving the rest.

J.   The Ten Actions

The ten actions below will help you overcome stress reactions and support you on a daily basis to keep resonating with your vision: accepting what is, letting go of regrets, maintaining your hope and optimism and persevering action in the face of all obstacles and failures.

(**mcs**) for the Action you need, or choose whatever action you intuitively feel will support you on a daily basis:

1. **Remind yourself of your vision**
   Write it down, read it, act on it in some small way.

2. **Breathing**
   Breathing slowly and deeply activates the parasympathetic nervous system, which calms the adrenal stress response and allows you to access your higher brain potential for self-healing and regeneration. Breathing in the left nostril and out of the right nostril calms the mind and clears negative thoughts.

3. **Stature of Power and Creativity**
   - Come into your stature/posture of power in relation to your vision

   - Mentally state your life vision and purpose

   - Say "thank you" to Source   *It is impossible to be grateful and unhappy at the same time!*

   - Love and let go of everything that is not love in your life

   - Take a deep-in-your-body loving breath

   - Arc your rainbow energy breath and vision out into the world

   - Take care of the details – what are the details in relation to your vision?

   - Take your time, find your own right pacing

   - Be conscious of your spirit, your true essence

4. **Drink pure water**
   Water flushes out toxins and acidity. During stressful situations we need to drink more water, which is also needed for conducting electrical impulses throughout the body.

5. **Cranial Contact on the prefrontals**
   Place the fourth, middle and index fingers on both hands lightly on your forehead (the higher brain prefrontal cortex), about halfway between your hairline and your eyebrows. This has a calming effect as it re-calibrates your cranial rhythms, which become disordered in stress response situations.

6. **Positive thoughts, words and actions**
   In a full-blown stress response, our thoughts are negative, we say things we regret and we become reactive.

   Negative thoughts set off our sympathetic nervous system adrenaline response and then the stress is further compounded with yet more negative thoughts, feelings and actions.

When in a stressful situation, think, say or do something positive and observe what happens: positive-feeling brain chemicals are released and a calming, relaxing, bonding, self-healing response is activated by our parasympathetic nervous system.

Many years ago Dan Millman, the author of *Way of the Peaceful Warrior,* related in a seminar how he was once crossing the Golden Gate Bridge while being tailgated by an impatient and angry man. There was nothing Dan could do to get out of his way. But when he reached the tollbooth, he paid both for himself and the tailgating car behind him. When the lady told the man that his toll had been paid for, the man's attitude instantly shifted: he started waving and smiling. This is the power of positive thoughts and actions, no matter what!

7. **Dance, yoga and walking**
Moving the large muscles of your arms and legs uses up excess mobilized adrenaline and cortisol hyperactive energy. These movements lead to endorphins of joy that boost your immune system and prevent adrenaline and cortisol from being deposited in your muscles and joints.

8. **ColorYourWorld Glasses**
ColorYourWorld Glasses use roscolene gels with the same frequencies developed by Dr. Dinshah in the 1930s for self-healing. Colored light is one of the most ancient and powerful of healing options. Color shifts our frequencies, how we perceive things and our brain responses. Green and blue glasses have a calming effect on the mind for instance.
See ResonanceRepatterning.net eStore for the ColorYourWorld Glasses

9. **Hugs and loving touch**
Hugs and loving touch activate the parasympathetic nervous system, which calms the stress response, supports digestion, regeneration and bonding.

10. **Acupuncture points without needles** *See I. p.46*

HOW TO USE THE FIVE SECRETS
IN YOUR DAILY LIFE
EVEN IF YOU HAVE NOT YET ATTENDED A RESONANCE REPATTERNING SEMINAR

When facing any challenge, do any of the following:

- Ask yourself, **"What is my vision in life? What is most important to me?"** Do an Energizing Option so you resonate once more with your vision. See ResonanceRepatterning.net > STORE for SPIRAL UP! 127 ENERGIZING OPTIONS TO BE YOUR BEST RIGHT NOW

- Immediately repeat – over and over – **"I accept what is, free of resistance."** If necessary, if you have the time, do an Energizing Option so you resonate with accepting what is, free of all resistance.

- If you hear yourself regretting anything, ask yourself, **"What am I regretting? What is the higher lesson for me in these regrets?"** Do an Energizing Option so you resonate with learning the lesson of the regret, so you can let go of your regrets and move on to bigger and better things.

- Do an Energizing Option for resonating with, **"I am hopeful and optimistic, no matter what."**

- Ask yourself, **"What positive action will support (*name your vision*) that I can do right now?"** Do an Energizing Option so you resonate with going into unhesitating action, however small, toward achieving your vision.

- Do one of the ten Positive Actions {J}.

- Do one or more of the Acupuncture points {I}.

RR SESSIONS: If you would like to receive the complete Repatterning with a professional Resonance Repatterning Practitioner, in person or over the phone, go to ResonanceRepatterning.net > Sessions for RR Institute Practitioners worldwide who have listed themselves on the RRI website.

RR SEMINARS: If you would like to attend Resonance Repatterning seminars in person or online, so you can use RR effectively on yourself and/or others, go to ResonanceRepatterning.net > Seminars for the list of teachers endorsed by the Resonance Repatterning Institute to teach.

3. THE POWER OF YOUR LIGHT – ACCESS IT, LIVE IT

'Bird, how can you fly in the gravity of this darkness?'
'Love lifts me.'

Rumi

The light not only from our sun but also from billions upon billions of similar stars is at exactly the right frequency for life as we know it to exist. If it was of a higher frequency – as in x-rays and gamma rays – living systems would be blown apart. If it was of a lower frequency, as in radio waves, its energy would be insufficient to be absorbed and utilized.

John Davidson
The Gospel of Jesus: In Search of His Original Teachings

Who we are is a field of light

Frequency or vibration consists of three aspects: sound, light and movement or vibration.

When the vibrating movement, sound and light of our frequencies are in harmony, we feel physically energized, we are in touch with our feelings of joy, love and gratitude, and our thoughts are positive, hopeful and uplifting.

When the vibrating movement, sound and light of our frequencies are diminished or non-coherent, we may have health problems or feel angry, afraid and depressed or have repetitive negative thoughts.

STORY OF JACQUES LUSSEYRAN

In his extraordinary book *And There Was Light,* Jacques Lusseyran describes how he became blind as the result of a childhood accident. Yet in spite of his total blindness, he could still see. He writes:

"As I walked along a country road bordered by trees, I could point to each one of the trees along the road, even if they were not spaced at regular intervals. I knew whether the trees were straight or tall ... or gathered into thickets and partly covering the ground around them."

How was this possible? Because, he explains, he was in touch with his own inner light and the light in all things.

Because of his connection to the frequencies of light, he could do everything that his schoolfriends could do, and more – not only did he hike, play games and study with the others at school, but as a teenager he also created and led a teenagers' resistance movement during WWII when the Nazis occupied Paris. Because he could see people's light, he interviewed each of the eight hundred teenagers who wanted to be part of the resistance, to see who was appropriate for the dangerous work of this underground movement.

There was one thing Lusseyran couldn't do and that was play a musical instrument. The frequencies or light colors he saw when he heard an instrument were too overwhelming for him. He describes his experience of sound and light in music:

"At concerts, for me, the orchestra ... flooded me with all the colors of the rainbow. If the violin came in by itself, I was suddenly filled with gold and fire, and with red so bright that I could not remember having seen it on any object. When it was the oboe's turn, a clear green ran all through me, so cool that I seemed to feel the breath of night.... Sounds and colors are being exchanged endlessly."

Feelings that amplify or diminish our light

Lusseyran discovered from his own personal experience what allowed him to stay connected to his light and see – in spite of his blindness – and what disconnected him from his light, making him truly blind. He describes this connection to and disconnection from his light:

"At every waking hour and even in my dreams I lived in a stream of light. There were times when the light faded, almost to the point of disappearing. It happened every time I was afraid. If, instead of letting myself be carried along by confidence I hesitated, then without exception I hit or wounded myself.... What the loss of my eyes had not accomplished was brought about by fear. It made me blind.

"Anger and impatience had the same effect, throwing everything into confusion. If I suddenly grew anxious to win, to be the first at all costs, then all at once I could see nothing.... I could no longer afford to be jealous or unfriendly, because as soon as I was, a bandage came down over my eyes.... But when I was happy and serene, approached people with confidence and thought well of them, I was rewarded with light. I always knew where the road was open and where it was closed. I had only to look at the bright signal which taught me how to live."

Any negative thought, negative feeling or even an attitude of unfriendliness cuts us off from our light. We may not experience it as dramatically as Lusseyran did – whose blindness became a reality when he spiraled down into negative thoughts and feelings – but in some way or another we do experience it.

Even if our physical eyes keep on seeing, there is some part of us that knows (by how we feel, or through physical sickness or emotional and mental loss of balance) that we have disconnected from the power of our light and the field of infinite possibilities – this field of universal energy that allowed Lusseyran to see even though he was blind.

~

Dr. Harry Sirota – glasses of light

Sometime back, I met the late Dr. Harry Sirota, a fascinating optometrist who developed a way to provide glasses that allowed more light to enter the eyes and brain.

At one point he told me to put on my old prescription glasses and to go up a flight of stairs. I walked up the stairs slowly, holding onto the banister. But when he put on my new Sirota light glasses and told me to go up the same flight of stairs, I spontaneously ran up and down and didn't touch the banister once.

Then, with my old prescription glasses on, he asked me to describe my mother. I commented that whatever argument I had, she would always come up with the opposite point of view. Then he put on my light glasses and told me to keep talking about her. Without a second thought, I said she was powerful and creative and how much I respected her. Back and forth we went: negative comments when wearing prescription glasses, positive comments when wearing my light glasses.

When we have more light in our field, it not only changes how we move and how we view other people, it also changes how we see the world around us. While standing in a courtyard wearing my new Sirota lenses, Dr. Sirota asked me to look around. Suddenly I could hear the fountain two courtyards away from where we were standing, and all the trees and flowers looked brilliant, shining. I became aware that I was smiling and feeling happy for no reason. Absorbing more light, my feelings changed and opened up to the beauty of life.

The importance of a highly vibrating field of light

The color waveband of the electromagnetic spectrum we experience is extremely narrow. The more highly vibrating our field of light, the more health we have, the more joy, the more options and possibilities we are open to, and the more pleasure we have in all that we see and experience. And the light we radiate benefits others in ways we may never be aware of.

The woman who sent out good thoughts

There is a story about a car accident that has changed my response to every accident I pass by. A woman in a serious car accident found herself floating above her body. She saw the line of cars blocked by the accident and heard what people were saying: "This is all we need!" said one driver. "Now we'll be late," said another. "Can you see anything?" asked a third.

Then the woman noticed a white light pouring from a car, connecting to where she floated. She was attracted to the car and inside she saw a woman praying for her. In her disembodied state she memorized the car's registration, and after she was discharged from the hospital she sent the lady a letter, thanking her for her good thoughts that had helped her reconnect to her light and to her body once more.

Now when I pass an accident, instead of impatience or anxiety or idle curiosity, I send a blessing, a good thought – "May you receive the inner strength and light you need for your healing." Such a little thing: a thought that expands our own field of light and supports the light of another.

We intuitively know what makes our light shine: it's when we are happy, serene, approach people with confidence and think well of others. And now we have seen what diminishes our light to a pinprick point of almost disappearing: fear, anger, impatience, being anxious to win and be first at all costs, jealousy, negative thoughts about ourselves and others and plain old unfriendliness.

Humanity has shared goals

The question is how does our light support us in achieving the vision and purpose of our life and the fundamental goals we all share in common?

Ultimately all human beings have similar goals:

- We all want to maintain our health and youthful vigor.

- We all want love and acceptance in our relationships.

- We all want a sense of contentment and peace of mind, no matter what the ups and downs of our life may be.

- We all want to be our best and achieve the best we are capable of. We want to make a positive difference for others.

- And there is an aspect of us – soul or spirit – that wants to access the field of infinite possibilities, or whatever we call the ocean of divine bliss. We want to integrate the higher qualities of love and peace. We want to find meaning and realize the purpose of our lives. We want to be of service.

How much we are able to move in the direction of these goals depends on the quality of our own vibrating field of light. How far we move away from these goals depends on how diminished our field of light is.

It is important that we know what we can do to expand our field of light. Expansion of our light – coherent light – makes us receptive to the field of infinite possibilities, which in turn brings us closer to achieving our shared goals.

The lesson of the non-swimming rats
A painful research project – for the rats that were used – also happens to have wisdom to teach us.

In this project some non-swimming rats were placed in a tank of water. They thrashed around until they were on the verge of drowning, at which point they were saved. Within one month of this daily treatment the young rats died of old age. The researchers thought their premature aging and death was due to the stress of facing death every day.

Looking at this experiment from the point of view of light provides a different interpretation. The rats went into fear and panic. Fear, as we know, diminishes our field of light – whether we are human or animal. Diminished light cuts us off from the field of infinite possibilities. If the rats had remained calm and serene – in other words, if they had maintained a strong field of light the way Lusseyran did – they would have connected to the field of infinite possibilities. At least one rat would then have discovered how to relax and float and the others would have picked up on the new learning.

When even one person or animal learns a new more coherent way of doing something, others – no matter how far apart they may be – make the same positive discovery. Instead of panic, stress, old age and death, the rats would have been calm and stress free – they could have floated and lived!

It is not stress that makes us prematurely age and die. It is when we don't handle our stress with power – with our light intact. This is what makes positive outcomes impossible, and makes us age or get sick.

Handling stress with optimism or giving in to fear and frustration

As we read in the second chapter, Ernest Shackleton, with a crew of twenty-seven men, attempted to cross Antarctica on foot. But before they could land, their ship became stuck in an ice flow and broke apart.

After eighteen months of surviving on ice flows that moved away from the frozen land towards the open ocean, Shackleton finally chose the only option for life – to sail with five of the men in a small open boat across eight hundred miles of the most dangerous ocean on earth, in subzero temperatures.

And when, against all possible odds, they landed on South Georgia island, three of them had to climb for thirty-six hours over unmapped mountains to reach the small Norwegian whaling village on the other side of the island.

Stress, fear and hopelessness turn our hair white

Shackleton's crew said that in spite of the superhuman intensity of these stresses, his hair remained brown. It was only during the four months that followed their successful arrival at the whaling village, when he couldn't find a ship to return to

Elephant Island to save the rest of the crew he had left behind there, that his hair turned white.

His frustration and anger at the British government for delays – in the middle of WWI – and his fear that his men would lose their lives finally diminished his light and the stress he couldn't handle with a sense of hope and optimism caused his premature aging.

Our light keeps us connected to the field of infinite possibilities and teaches us right action and optimism as it guides every moment of our lives. Again, this is what we see in Ernest Shackleton. His crew said that he always stayed calm and optimistic in the face of every obstacle and shock. His only intention was to bring each member of his crew safely back home. This was the light that guided him.

Connected to the power of his light, he and the crew survived one superhuman challenge after another and the impossible became possible. He saved the lives of the entire crew.

The lesson of the wingless insects

Some researchers had just completed a project that involved some wingless insects, which were left to die on a dead bush outside the back door of the lab. To the amazement of the researchers, in the face of possible death the insects grew wings and flew away.

Our lives, then, are not about being free from stress, but about growing wings – letting go of all limitations, negative judgments, feelings and attitudes, so we stay connected to the light of right intention and action, which make us receptive to *anything is possible*.

Two possibilities for how we live

The first possibility is the rat possibility.
It has five aspects, which we may recognize in our lives:

1. **We are stuck in wanting a difficult situation we are in to be other than it is.** Like the rats we thrash around wanting our situation to be different.

2. **We go into negative feelings, thoughts and responses to our difficult situation** – like the rats. Whether it's fear, anger, hopelessness, blame, judgments or unfriendliness, it makes no difference. Any negative feeling diminishes our light to one extent or another.

3. **Our light is diminished as a result of our negative responses and feelings**, which makes it impossible to access the field of infinite possibilities – our source of strength and inner guidance that allows us to do even what appears to be impossible.

4. As a consequence, **we resonate with non-coherent reactions, make poor choices, going into hasty actions that don't help us**. We may react with anger and, similar to the rats, thrash around in our same old quarrels and differences, or regretting something that has happened, perhaps for a lifetime. Or we thrash around in blame, wanting the other person to change. Day after day, controlled by our own reactiveness, we remain unaware that floating or swimming – options that work – even exist!

5. **We live in a state of stress, premature aging and early death.**
   We see this happening all around us.

   Research has proven that most illnesses, if not all of them, are caused by stress (distress): people in their forties with heart trouble; twenty-year-olds with hardening of the arteries; diabetes, obesity, cancer, exhaustion, daily headaches, depression, accidents, alcohol and drug abuse – to name just a few. Symptoms, no matter what our age, are signals of diminished, non-coherent light: we are not receiving light and we are not radiating our light.

   We take it for granted that people are elderly and die in their eighties. Yet there are population groups around the world where the majority are healthy at well over a hundred!

The second possibility is the wingless insect possibility.
It too has five aspects, which one day we will hopefully recognize in our lives:
1. **We accept the present situation we are in, however difficult it appears to be.** It is what it is. "I accept (*whatever the difficult situation is*) free of all

resistance." Acceptance keeps us receptive to the field of limitless possibilities within. Whereas resistance blocks the flow of energy and makes self-healing slow or impossible.

2. **We have positive feelings, thoughts and responses in whatever challenging situation we are in** – whether calmness, courage, understanding, optimism or friendliness makes no difference, as long as it is a positive response. Our positive responses amplify the frequencies of our light. A positive attitude keeps us connected to our light, which boosts our immune system and gives us the strength to face our challenges.

3. **We are free of inappropriate reptilian brain fight-flight reactions and inappropriate limbic brain emotional discharging reactions**. In this way our light is amplified because there is no resistance from these negative responses to cancel out our light frequencies.

4. Because of the lack of negative resistance, **we are open and receptive to the field of infinite possibilities**:
   - We see or intuit different options.

   - We recognize that we are responsible for our own right actions, which are based on what our conscience knows is ethical.

   - We act free of regrets, letting go of past regrets as we move forward to a better future based on what we have learned.

   - We resonate with choices that help us and others. Like the wingless insects, we grow wings and fly.

5. **We live in a state of joy, youthful health and vigor into old age**.
   The late Paul C. Bragg epitomized this way of living. Even at one hundred years of age he was still running and surfing Hawaiian waves!

   A man who recently died at 113 in good health was asked the secret of his health. He said he never got into conflict with anyone. He worked in his small garden. He walked two miles a day, ate simple vegetarian food – less food as he got older – and he meditated many hours each day.

Each of us needs to find our own way of doing what it takes to expand our field of light on every level. And we need to avoid doing what diminishes our light physically, emotionally, mentally and spiritually.

Our world is insubstantial

Professor Varela, professor of cognitive science at the Institute of Neurosciences in Paris, said: "Once you accept that your world-universe is non-substantial yet exists, there is an enormous opening for possibilities to create and change."

From the point of view of **Resonance Repatterning**, what Professor Varela is saying is that when we accept that our world is made up of energy frequencies, **we can change our reality by changing the frequencies we resonate with.**

In THE POWER OF YOUR LIGHT REPATTERNING, we will look at how to resonate with expanding our light and how to change our resonance with what blocks or diminishes our light.

Professor Varela adds, "Our world, our communities, our organizations, will change only if we change."

Resonance Repatterning is about personal change and the positive impact this has on our life:

- Resonance Repatterning is a system for identifying the unconscious frequency patterns we resonate with – the negative beliefs and feelings in response to past experiences – that lock us into limitation and diminish our light.

- Resonance Repatterning helps us resonate with expanding our field of light so we can change who we are and how we act in the present – grow wings and fly, rather than continue to thrash around in stress reactions that lead to illness and premature death.

We can only give what we have. As we strengthen our own field of light, we automatically support others to do the same.

With each tiny shift towards positive resonance, our families, our communities and our world automatically benefit from the changes each of us makes that amplify our field of light.

FURTHER READING

Caroline Alexander. *The Endurance: Shackleton's Legendary Antarctic Expedition.* New York, NY: Alfred A. Knopf, 2006.

John Davidson. *The Gospel of Jesus: In Search of His Original Teachings.* Rockport, Maine: Element Books, 1995.

Jacques Lusseyran. *And There Was Light.* New York, NY: Parabola Books, 1987.

Chloe Wordsworth. *A New Vision.* Scottsdale, AZ: Resonance Publishing, 1998. *Includes a chapter on Dr. Harry Sirota as well as Repatternings for Light.*

I have heard that there is a man in Mexico who trains blind children to see by connecting them to their light.

3.

THE POWER OF YOUR LIGHT REPATTERNING

THE POWER OF YOUR LIGHT REPATTERNING

A. Read or tell the story of Jacques Lusseyran *p.54*

Ask, "What does this story mean for you?" *[**cr**]with "I (*name the positive meaning*)" (*will be off/umb off*).

B. Identify the negative situation

Do {a–b} in sequence.

a. *Ask,* "What situation are you not happy about – you are reacting negatively or you feel upset?"

*[**cr**] (*will be on/umb on because the upset or lack of clarity is diminishing client's light*).

b. Identify the non-acceptance

*[**cr**] with, "I don't accept (*name the situation*) for what it is. I want it to be different" (*will be on/umb on because at the moment client resonates with non-acceptance and the diminished light that results*).

C. Name the negative feelings and thoughts

(**mcs**) {a–h} for the ones needed.

Understanding the negative feeling response

Any negative response you resonate with is a signal that your light is diminished. Reacting negatively to any life situation is a downward spiral. Once your light is amplified and coherent in relation to your present situation, you will automatically respond positively and confidently, no matter how difficult the present situation may be.

a. (mcs) Anger feelings need to be identified?

Ask, "What are you angry about?"

*[**cr**] with, "I feel (angry ● irritated ● impatient) that (*name the apparent cause of your anger feelings*) and I diminish my light" (*will be on/umb on*).

b. **(mcs) Blame and judgmental feelings need to be identified?**
Ask, "What do you blame (*name the person involved*) for in this upsetting situation?"
*[**cr**] with, "I blame and judge (*name person*) for (*name the blame and judgments*) and I diminish my light" *(will be on/umb on).*

c. **(mcs) Fear feelings need to be identified?**
Ask, "What fears come up for you in this situation?"
*[**cr**] with "I'm afraid that (*name fear*) and I diminish my light" *(will be on/umb on).*

d. **Put-downs need to be identified?**
Ask, "In this situation how do you put down (*name person*) or yourself?"
*[**cr**] with, "I put down (*name person/myself*) when I say/do (*name what is said/done*) and I diminish my light" *(will be on/umb on).*

e. **Competition needs to be identified?**
Ask, "How are you competitive with (*name person*), wanting to be top, the best, to receive more acknowledgment, etc.?"
*[**cr**] with "I (*name the non-coherent competition or actions*) and I diminish my light" *(will be on/umb on).*

Understanding non-coherent competition versus true competition
Non-coherent competition is when we need to win every argument, have the last word, need to be right, when we want our own way and want to run the show, and when we compete to receive attention and be more powerful than others.

True competition is like a runner who has a pacer. The pacer motivates the runner to keep going and raises the bar on the speed that is possible for the runner. True competition is always inspiring because it challenges each person – whether in the action or observing the action – to reach beyond what they thought was possible for them to be or achieve.

f. Inadequacy needs to be identified?
Ask, "How do you feel inadequate in relation to (*name person*)?"
*[**cr**] with, "I diminish my light through feeling inadequate in relation to (*name person's apparent superior qualities*)" *(will be on/umb on).*

g. Victim position needs to be identified?
Ask, "How do you feel helpless and hopeless in this situation?"
*[**cr**] with, "I feel (*name the helpless, hopeless feelings*) and I diminish my light" *(will be on/umb on).*

h. Unfriendliness needs to be identified?
Ask, "In what way do you feel unfriendly towards (*name the person*)?"
*[**cr**] with "I (*name the unfriendly thoughts, words or actions*) and I diminish my light" *(will be on/umb on).*

D. Identify the consequences of the diminished light
(**mcs**) {a–f} for the one(s) needed.
*[**cr**] *(will be on/umb on because at the moment client resonates with these consequences).*

a. I don't see any other options, so I keep repeating what I am doing that isn't working for me.
b. I don't know (how to change this situation • what to change in this situation).
c. I'm stuck doing what (isn't helping me/others • is creating more stress for me)• (I make poor choices • I go into hasty actions that don't benefit me or anyone else).
d. (I am stressed out • I feel unwell • I feel prematurely old • I get into accidents • I attempt to self-medicate with alcohol and/or drugs).
e. I don't have the strength to handle the present situation correctly.
f. I feel cut off from my inner guidance.

E. The earlier experience

Do {a–e} in sequence.

a. *Ask,* "What earlier experience do you feel is similar to the present situation with (*name person*)?"

*[**cr**] with "(*Name the earlier experience*) diminishes my light and I continue to diminish my light in the present" *(will be on/umb on because client still resonates with this experience from the past diminishing his/her light in the present).*

b. *Ask,* "What negative feeling did you have when (*name the earlier experience*)?"

*[**cr**] with "I continue to feel (*name feeling*) in the present" *(will be on/ umb on).*

c. *Ask,* "What negative belief(s) do you have about yourself/others as a result of that painful experience?"

*[**cr**] with "I continue to diminish my light in the present by believing (*name the negative belief*) to be true" *(will be on/umb on).*

d. *Ask,* "What is the result of this negative belief in your life and relationships?"

*[**cr**] *(will be on/umb on).*

e. *Ask,* "What do you want instead of this past memory frequency?"

Explain: "Everything is in the mind. You can continue to live with this past frequency that diminishes your light, or you can amplify and strengthen your light in the present. By creating a positive memory thought, you activate new brain-nerve pathways for what you want instead."

*[**cr**] *(will be off/umb off).*

F. Identify amplifying client's light through acceptance

*[**cr**] with "I accept (*name the present situation*) free of all resistance" *(will be off/umb off because client does not resonate with amplifying his/her light through acceptance and trust).*

G. Identify amplifying client's light through positive responses
(**mcs**) {a–e} for the one(s) needed.

    a. *Ask,* "What positive response can you have in relation to (*name the situation/person*)?"
*[**cr**] (will be off/umb off).*

    b. *[**cr**] with "I bring (creativity • understanding • optimism • friendliness • trust • respect • a sense of safety) to the situation with (*name person*), which amplifies our light" *(will be off/umb off).*

    c. *[**cr**] with "(I avoid conflict with (*name person*), while also following my conscience and doing right actions • I act free of regrets)" *(will be off/ umb off).*

    d. *[**cr**] with "I avoid emotional reactiveness with (*name person*) and trust there are important lessons for me in what is happening" *(will be off/ umb off).*

    e. *[**cr**] with "(I see positive options • I am receptive to extraordinary outcomes)" *(will be off/umb off).*

H. Identify the smile factor
*[**cr**] with, "I radiate my light by greeting (*name person*) and all people with a smile from my heart. All beings are my friend" *(will be off/umb off).*

Understanding the smile factor
In the old days, and perhaps even now, when a Native American met a rattlesnake on his path he would stop. Standing in silence he would greet the rattlesnake as a brother and friend. After a while both would go on their way in peace.

If you feel that anyone is your enemy, your light is diminished and either you and/or the other person will be hurt. When you greet everyone as a friend, a brother or sister, your light is amplified. The result, in one way or another, will be positive. It is interesting that robbers admitted they would not rob a 7/11 store if the attendant greeted them with a smile. This is the power of our light, which is expressed and amplified through a smile!

I. Living in the light with joy, optimism and gratitude

Ask, "Do you want to be healthy and full of energy, to have love and acceptance in all your relationships, even the ones that are difficult for you, to achieve your best and do your best in all you do and to live with positive thoughts and feelings that amplify your light?"

If the answer is yes, (**mcs**) {a–g} for the one(s) needed.
*[**cr**] *(will be off/umb off because client does not resonate with amplifying his/her light in relation to this high ideal).*

a. I am confident, happy, serene and think well of people.

b. I do, say and think those things that amplify my light.

c. When I (do • say • think) something negative that diminishes my light, (I get to the cause and transform my resonance with this negativity • I use my prefrontal willpower and positive intention to stop what I am (doing • saying • thinking) and I get back on track with living in the light).

d. In every situation I tune in to the field of limitless possibilities and am receptive to *Anything is possible.*

e. I walk every day and see beauty.

f. I eat healthy food (organic and as much fruit and vegetables as possible) and I avoid processed junk foods, soft drinks, sugar and alcohol, which diminish my light.

g. I am grateful (for my life • for each person I know/meet • for being energized in nature • for my health • for each positive thought • for each moment of stillness and calmness of mind • for each kind action I am graced to do for others • for the willpower to use my energy for what is positive and uplifting • for every positive intention I put into action and live).

J. Identify the Energizing Option needed to shift the resonance identified in this session

(**mcs**) for the Energizing Option from the SPIRAL UP! book that is needed for shifting the resonance patterns identified in this Repatterning.

If you are a Resonance Repatterning practitioner, you will then recheck the *[**cr**] statements to confirm the change.

HOW TO USE THE POWER OF YOUR LIGHT REPATTERNING IN YOUR DAILY LIFE
EVEN IF YOU HAVE NOT YET ATTENDED A RESONANCE REPATTERNING SEMINAR

- Experiment with going for a walk each day and smiling from the heart to each person you meet.

- When you next meet an obstacle or difficulty, take a pause, avoid reacting negatively and say "I accept free of all resistance." Do an Energizing Option from SPIRAL UP! to resonate with this attitude.

- When you next deal with a 'problem' person, avoid negative thoughts, feelings and gossiping about him/her and ask yourself, "What is the higher learning (*name person*) is bringing me?" Say to yourself "I am grateful for the learning (*name person*) brings me." Do an Energizing Option from SPIRAL UP! to resonate with this attitude.

- When dealing with a difficult situation/person, ask yourself, "What earlier experience does this remind me of?" Then say, "My present is different from my past. I choose to amplify my light in the present." Do an Energizing Option from SPIRAL UP! to resonate with this attitude.

- Take two or three letters from the Repatterning: {B} plus one or two others, and then do an Energizing Option from SPIRAL UP! to change your resonance with the information you have identified in those letters.

RR SESSIONS: *If you would like to receive the complete Repatterning with a professional Resonance Repatterning Practitioner, in person or over the phone, go to ResonanceRepatterning.net > Sessions for RR Institute Practitioners worldwide who have listed themselves on the RRI website.*

RR SEMINARS: *If you would like to attend Resonance Repatterning seminars in person or online, so you can use RR effectively on yourself and/or others, go to ResonanceRepatterning.net > Seminars for the list of teachers endorsed by the Resonance Repatterning Institute to teach.*

4. ANGER AS A BLESSING – QUANTUM LEAP TO A NEW WAY OF BEING

We are disturbed not by what happens to us but by our thoughts about what happens to us.

Epictetus – First century CE
Greek Mystic, Stoic School

Always love is a medium through which man contacts and applies the creative principle of the universe. And what love is allowed to create through man is up to man himself. His love attitude determines the course taken by the creative principle. Inevitably, the creative principle operating on and through man creates something; something noble or ignoble, constructive or destructive.

Starr Daily, *Love Can Open Prison Doors*

Anger is a huge issue in almost everyone's life. We react with irritation, impatience and anger when driving, at home, at work – and of course in the world, where anger manifests as war and abuse of nature.

How can we get to the bottom of this emotional response that is so destructive for each of us personally, as well as for our relationships?

People who can see our field of light say that if we knew what anger did to us, we would never get angry for any reason.

Intellectually we may even recognize that anger diminishes our field of light and blinds us to our higher mind and spirit – to the field of unconditional love – and yet too often we still react with irritation or outright anger.

As we saw in the "The Power of Your Light," Jacques Lusseyran – totally blind as a result of a childhood accident – could 'see' because he saw the light of each object and person. But he also discovered that if he became afraid or angry, his light would be diminished almost to the point of disappearing. When he could no longer see his light, this was when he truly became blind.

Anger and fear are two of the major ways we diminish our light. Looking more deeply at the emotion of anger, we may also see how it holds a blessing for us. Using our awareness of anger can help us get back on track with amplifying our field of light, making us receptive to a new way of being.

All vibrations radiate light or color, and sound too. If we had the eyes to see and the ears to hear, we would experience the color and sound of every movement we make, every thought, every feeling. Some colors and sounds are beautiful – like the gorgeous colors Lusseyran would see when he listened to an orchestra playing classical music. Other sounds, thoughts and emotions exude colors that are not so beautiful.

Like a radio receiver, if we attune to harmonious frequencies, we experience health, happiness, joy and positive ways of thinking and acting. If we are tuned to dissonant frequencies, we may live with poor health and other negatives in our life and relationships.

To discover the blessing in anger, let's look at anger from two points of view: First, the point of view of the Chinese Five Elements of Acupuncture. And second, the point of view of the 'creative principle.'

Five Elements of Chinese Acupuncture

One of the Five Elements of Chinese Acupuncture is called the Wood Element. Wood is associated with springtime, new life, hope, new beginnings, growth, optimism – and anger.

From the point of view of the Five Elements, our anger and frustration let us know we want something to *change*: some growth that is not happening, perhaps a new beginning or a need that is not being met. If a change is needed or we feel unable to grow and expand in a certain direction, more often than not we'll feel frustrated and angry.

All the little things in life that irritate us – what was said or not said, done or not done, the toothpaste that was squeezed in the wrong way, the trash that wasn't taken out and the other million reasons for getting angry – are saying something about our own Wood Element.

None of these irritants are the real reason for our frustration or anger. That's why nothing changes. Even if the other person starts squeezing the toothpaste in the correct way, there will always be something else that will create irritation and anger.

Our Wood Element wants growth and positive change. It also wants belligerence to be transformed into benevolence – by transcending right and wrong thinking and all judgments. Our anger reaction tells us there is some inner growth, some inner change we ourselves need that isn't happening. Our anger reaction is trying to get our attention: time to wake up!

But we ignore this wake-up call because we perceive that whatever is irritating us is someone else's fault. They are the cause of our anger: you've asked your child or spouse to take the trash out ten times and finally you blow your top. Their fault? Absolutely! But not so.

Anger as a mirror turned outward

Anger is like a mirror. If we turn the mirror of our mind and anger outward, someone else will always be the cause of our anger.

For instance, we are waiting at the traffic light and the green lights up and the car in front doesn't move. We start out with impatience: "Come on!" But if the driver is on his or her cell phone and still doesn't move, we quickly go into irritation and perhaps full-blown anger: we may start honking our horn and before we know it we are shouting in our mind, if not with our voice. Some people go into road rage. Whatever the reaction, we are convinced the other driver is to blame for our irritation and upset.

But what if we had chosen to relax, breathe deeply and say to our self, "I have all the time in the world. Relax, driver in front on me. Take your time and have a wonderful day!" In India, drivers cut in front of each other all the time. This is the accepted way of driving and people rarely get upset. It doesn't cross their mind to get angry!

Others don't force us to think and feel in a relaxed and happy way or in an impatient angry way. We make our own choice in how we think and feel in response to others' behavior. However, when people are kind and behave thoughtfully, life is much easier for all concerned!

Anger as a mirror turned inward

If we turn the mirror of our mind and anger inward, then we blame ourselves for everything that happens: the divorce is my fault; it's my fault that my child is sick; it's my fault that my spouse isn't happy.

This anger at ourselves in the form of self-blame causes us to live with guilt and too easily turns into depression and hopelessness – an angry hopeless depression. This inward-turned anger is based on the feeling there is nothing we can do to create positive change within ourselves and our life.

Both types of blame – blaming others or ourselves – diminish our light.

Blaming others or blaming ourselves with anger involves negative judgments. It's the blame and these judgments that diminish our field of light. When our light is diminished, we may experience this disconnect as depression, exhaustion, drug or alcohol abuse, accidents, an unhappy marriage, a migraine headache or some other sickness, or as not getting the promotion we wanted and expected.

Whatever the outward manifestation, it is the tip of the iceberg. Underneath there is a frustrated desire for some growth and positive change – some inner growth that we ourselves need – that isn't happening.

Four stages in the downward spiral of anger

- **Stage one:** We **blame** the other person or ourselves for what is wrong.

- **Stage two**: We have negative **judgments** about the person or ourselves.

- **Stage three**: We start to **dislike** the person we are judging and blaming – whether it's a stranger in the car in front of us, a difficult person at work, the person we are married to or our self. Not only dislike; sometimes dislike turns to hatred.

- **Stage four:** We go into **negative actions** – conflict, gossip, cutting off the relationship, verbal abuse or physical-sexual-emotional-mental abuse. On the national level this blame, judgment and hatred leads to bullying; abuse of women, minorities, animals and the environment; discrimination, crime and war.

What happens on the big scale – the macro level – starts with what happens on the individual scale – the micro level within us.

World peace – the macro level – starts with looking at our own personal daily downward spirals: our angry reactions, blame, judgments, dislike and negative actions in relation to ourselves and others. If we are not at peace within ourselves, we can never have peace outside.

On the micro level, our diminished field of light from our unresolved anger has consequences in terms of our health and relationships.

This is the bad news. But there is also good news!

The creative principle

We see in the first point of view that our anger requires us to bring our Wood Element back into balance and harmony so we can do our own inner work of growing towards the light.

The Wood Element wants us to evolve, to raise our consciousness, to strive for the best within ourselves. It insists that we stay directed towards the light that is within, which enables us to see positive options and the big picture, to remain optimistic and hopeful no matter what the external situation may be and to go into constructive action.

When we are on track, directed towards the light within, we won't blame or judge anyone for anything.

The second point of view that makes anger a blessing involves how we use the creative principle or the field of infinite possibilities.

When I was ten years old, my father brought home a book by a man called Starr Daily. The book was called *Love Can Open Prison Doors*. Starr Daily's story and his description of the creative principle had a great impact on me.

STORY OF LOVE CAN OPEN PRISON DOORS

In the 1920s, at the age of twelve, Starr Daily committed a series of minor crimes. By the age of fourteen he was a confirmed criminal. He spent years in and out of prison and finally received a long-term sentence. He was angry, violent and filled with hatred for everything and everyone, including God.

Then something happened that changed the course of his life. He was given two weeks in solitary confinement, in what the prisoners called the dungeon. He says of this experience: "It was in the middle of an exceptionally bitter winter. The torture chamber was damp and foul and dark. The stone walls were full of frost; the concrete floors were wet and icy. You were put into a cell with nothing but a thin, much-washed shirt and overalls. Your shoes were taken away, but you were allowed to retain your socks. At night the keeper of the dungeon brought you a thin and filthy cotton blanket."

Eating nothing but bread and water, emaciated and close to death, he still refused to admit his guilt about a rule he was accused of breaking – which in fact he had not broken. In a state of dreamy delirium, a thought flashed through his mind: where would such determination of will end if it were directed differently...

A few days later he had a vision in which he felt utterly enveloped in love. He found himself exuding love. As he describes it, this love "seemed to pour from me in the form of some mighty sense of blissful gratitude, not for any one thing or things, but for all things, for life." As a result of this vision of love, he lost all awareness of his dungeon walls and his hunger, cold and suffering.

Then unexpected things began to happen. Suddenly the prison doctor stopped by three times in one day, asking him how he was doing. Each time Starr Daily told him he'd never felt better. Then the keeper of the dungeon, who had a violent dislike for him, came to his door and offered to smuggle in a sandwich from the officers' dining room. Starr Daily, who had once hated this man and now felt nothing but love for him, thanked him and explained that he wasn't hungry.

At this point he began to have an all-consuming compassion for the deputy warden who had sworn that Starr Daily would never come out of the dungeon until he crawled to him on his knees and whined and begged like a dog to be released.

About three days after his vision, the deputy warden himself came to his cell door and told him to go to the hospital to clean up and rest.

Love had opened his prison door and was to continue doing so in a hundred different ways until he was released from prison eleven years early, never to commit a crime again.

~

The most powerful force in existence – the creative principle

This amazing story, published in 1947, is true. Beyond the story itself, Starr Daily brings a deep understanding of what he calls **the creative principle,** which gives us insight into the blessing of anger.

Basically what Starr Daily says is that love is the most powerful creative force in existence – something we may accept intellectually even if we haven't experienced the force of love in reality, as he did.

But, he says, what we love or desire determines how we use this creative principle of love – whether to worship God, for service, to achieve success in the world, or for crime.

He says that according to our desires, we can use this creative principle of love either for degradation or for upliftment.

Starr Daily drew on this power of love for a life of crime – and then drew on this same creative principle of love for integrity, right action, a life of spiritual uplift, healing and service. In both cases it was the same creative principle of unconditional love.

How to use this force

When we get angry with our spouse, child, boss, friend or anyone else who frustrates us, we are using the force of unconditional love – the creative principle – in a destructive way that diminishes our light and also diminishes the light of the person we are angry with. We are using this power of love to blame, judge, dislike and suffer.

If we observe how we respond to our work and what we do during the day, we may find we often focus on the negative. This means we are using the creative principle of unconditional love to support the negative in our life. According to our thoughts and actions, we either become more conscious of the creative principle of love or less conscious of it.

Anger cuts us off from being conscious of this field of love, of which we are a part.

If we are unconscious of the creative principle of love, it is like being in a coma. The real purpose of our anger and the blessing of anger is to become more conscious of the creative principle of love and how to channel or use this creative principle in positive uplifting ways.

The opportunity

Everything that makes us upset, impatient, irritated or angry is an opportunity for reconnecting to the creative principle of unconditional love within ourselves. This is what growth or evolution is all about. This is the potential of our Wood Element.

It is our lack of awareness of the creative principle of love that acts out as anger. If instead of anger concerning toothpaste and taking the trash out – or even with more serious issues – we manage to connect with the creative principle of unconditional love, we might look within ourself and discover that we need to grow in some way. Perhaps we are not taking time to relax, or to relax with our partner, to be away from work, the computer, cell phone, texting and our constant busyness – time to open our heart and just be.

But how do we deal with the reality of the daily irritations where some change is definitely required and is not happening? What do we do when someone is hurting someone else, using abusive words, gossiping about us at work and damaging our reputation? This is the reality we all face in one way or another.

How do we balance our Wood Element by resonating with the creative principle of love no matter what?

The power of resonance

Resonance is the bottom line for dealing with the daily nitty-gritty issues that irritate us or make us angry, so we can evolve within ourselves.

This is what Starr Daily did in prison. And it is what we are challenged to do in our own life.

Five steps for using the creative principle and resonance
Step one – awareness of the creative principle
Someone does something that upsets us or makes us feel angry and betrayed. Or someone is blaming, judging and disliking us. One choice is to use the creative principle of love by reacting in the same way with blame, judgment and dislike.

But we also other options: instead of going into our usual reaction of quarrels, conflict, withdrawing and cutting off – we can choose, as Starr Daily did in prison, to become aware of the creative principle of unconditional love and

- find something to love about the other person – *anything* that activates our love and compassion.

- and find something to love about ourself.

How can I feel compassion for this person and myself? No words. Just inner connection to the field of infinite possibilities for love. The field – the creative principle – moves according to our thoughts and feelings. We determine the direction it takes us in: either into anger, dislike, hate, pain and separation or into understanding, love and a sense of closeness, compassion and union.

The choice is ours.

Our anger/dislike is signaling us that we have disconnected from our awareness of the creative principle. We can use the power of the creative principle of unconditional love in any way we want – to justify why we are right and the other person is wrong, to blame, criticize, undermine, gossip, judge... or to make a different choice.

If we want to experience the field of love – the creative principle of unconditional love that is who we are in our core that resolves all differences and pain – we need to make the choice for union rather than the choice for separation.

Anger is about separation. But deep inside ourselves we all want understanding, love and union: that is the light we yearn for and are all growing towards.

So in our daily life, facing our frustrated unmet needs and expectations, our hurts and disappointments, we are challenged to choose between separation or union, anger or the creative principle of love that evaporates all differences and fills us with gratitude, healing and light.

Step two – the underlying issue

After we are aware of the creative principle of unconditional love and compassion and feel it in whatever minute way we can manage, then comes the second step: to get in touch with the underlying issue *within ourself* – nothing to do with the other person and what they are doing and saying or not doing and not saying.

The situation is telling us there is some inner place where *we* need to grow. So we use the situation – trash bags, toothpaste, negative behaviors, addictions – to recognize what the situation is bringing up for us that we have been avoiding: a positive attitude we need to embody, a positive action we need to take, a communication of what would make a positive difference for us, honestly sharing our needs and concerns free of blame, setting clear boundaries or something we need to integrate into our life and relationships.

For instance, someone shared with me that she asked her husband what he thought of my LIVING IN TUNE web radio show on stress reactions and how stress floods our system with cortisol. Her husband said, "Well, it looks like you've got more cortisol in your system than I do." She got furious, *felt diminished* and they ended up in a big argument!

So the question for her to ask herself would be, "What is this situation telling me about where I need to evolve and grow – some place where I lack something, some new way of being and acting, a higher state of consciousness that I need to integrate?"

I didn't go into this with her, but it could be that her place of growth was about self-esteem – **respecting herself or feeling respected and appreciated.** If she resonated with respecting and appreciating herself, then her husband saying that she had more cortisol in her system than he did wouldn't have made her angry. She might have laughed and agreed with him or disagreed with him. But not with anger.

If self-respect is the growth in consciousness she needs, she will need to resonate with it and go into action at every opportunity to embody self-respect. This action will lead her to appreciate and respect others, and from that she will be able to receive the appreciation and respect from others that she longs for. We can only receive from others what we resonate with giving to ourselves and to others.

To summarize:

Step one is to avoid blame, judgment, dislike, and negative words and actions and do our best to stay conscious of the creative principle of unconditional love by *finding something to love about the other.*

Step two is to get in touch with *what the situation invites us to learn about ourselves* – some growth or personal change that we ourselves need.

Step three involves getting in touch with *a need from our past that was not met at that time and is being triggered by the present situation*, resulting in the reactive anger response.

For instance, if your need for safety was not met as a child, you won't resonate with safety in your present relationships. Over and over again you will feel unsafe, unprotected – and all the irritation and anger in the world won't satisfy your need for the safety and protection you need and long for.

Now in the present you have the opportunity to change that negative resonance and reconnect to the field of unconditional love so you resonate with safety and protection.

Many of us have gone through experiences when we feel betrayed by a friend or business partner. We get angry, we blame the other person and we may even break off the relationship.

We disconnect from the creative principle of unconditional love for the other and ourselves. We don't get in touch with what the situation is inviting us to learn about ourselves – our place of evolution. And we don't get in touch with the earlier experience and our resonance with unmet needs and the negative feelings and beliefs that resulted from the need not being met.

As a result we find ourselves repeating betrayal experiences in one way or another, with one person after another – always feeling as though it is their fault.

Step four is to ask ourselves: "What positive habit or thought do I need to integrate into my life? Who do I want to be, how do I want to be? What action do I need to take?"

With anger, blame and judgments we always want the *other* person to change. With step four we find out what *we* need to do – how do *I* need to change.

For instance, in the example about taking out the trash, the wife's positive habit would *not* be to take out the trash in a state of fury! That would be just more of what she was already doing: busy, busy, busy being superwoman, "I'll do it all!"

The positive habit might have been to relax, do less, appreciate the husband more, stop blaming and judging and wanting him to change. That would have been a good beginning.

We may not know the best habit to put into action. It takes thought and insight to recognize the real habit we need to integrate. But in the Blessing of Anger Repatterning the questions and the muscle checking tool help identify the exact habit the situation is asking us to integrate and how to bring more consciousness of the creative principle of love into our lives.

Step five involves handling the reality of the upset with communication. Anger closes the lines of harmonious communication. Step five is about opening our heart to listen and share with understanding.

Our mistake is that we try to do step five first, which rarely works. Step five – the three communications – needs to be done **after** completing steps one through four.

In Resonance Repatterning we usually do the three communication steps in a session to make sure we resonate with them before we communicate with the person involved.

As our resonance changes, we get more adept at using the three communications in every situation. But if we do them before we have changed our resonance, we may find ourselves in yet another argument!

The three communications

1. Communicate what the person did in an "I" statement that is free of blame and judgment. For instance, in the case of the trash, we could say to our partner or child, "I notice there are three bags of trash that haven't been emptied." *Facts only, no feelings.*

2. Next: Communicate the real feeling – not just "I'm angry." That's not the real feeling. Again, in the trash example the wife might say, "I feel anxious that it won't be done and that I'll feel it's my responsibility to do it." *Again, no judgment or blame. Just owning our own real feelings.*

3. Now communicate the real need – the specific thing you want or need and the positive feeling you have when this need is met. This is not about saying, "I need you to take out the trash!" That is not the real need. For instance, the wife might say, "I need help doing the household chores. When you empty the trash every night I feel supported by you." So in this case it isn't about the trash at all. It's about needing help and support.

For many of us, feeling supported is a major **unmet need from our childhood.** In our childhood, the sense of help and support we needed from our parents wasn't always there. In my own case, my parents were busy running a school in the middle of WWII with bombs dropping, so I grew up feeling that I needed to take care of myself. For others, it would be a different problem. But in all cases, the result may be that we don't resonate with support being available when we need it. And in response we become superwoman/superman, taking care of everything – or feeling like a victim, that no one is there to take care of us.

When the past is superimposed on present relationships in this way, we will see problems – and often anger.

As we do our own inner work to change our resonance and become more conscious of the creative principle, we move into a new way of being.

This is the blessing of anger – the quantum leap to a new way of being based on the creative principle of unconditional love and how we use this principle either to take us in a negative or a positive direction – away from the light of our being or towards it.

What if positive change still doesn't happen in spite of the creative principle of love?

This brings up the question of how someone like Starr Daily, who didn't have a method and tool like Resonance Repatterning, was able to change his resonance with his past unmet needs and negative thoughts and feelings. How did he create the one-hundred-and-eighty degree turn around in his life?

Changing resonance through unconditional love

Unconditional love ultimately heals all negative resonance patterns. It leaps over all four steps! But we need to remember that Starr Daily had to go through intense suffering to the point of near death for him to become receptive to that ocean of love within himself, followed by years of inner work and service – putting love into action by volunteering to work in the prison TB ward, for instance, where he looked after the sick and dying.

Starr Daily was a dramatic case, an example and inspiration for us. Not only did he change through love, but through his own heightened consciousness and evolution, those he lived with in prison also changed dramatically.

We can only give what we ourselves have experienced. The prison inmates became receptive to their own self-healing through Starr Daily's connection to the creative principle of unconditional love. He didn't use words. Simply who he was, who he had become, created transformation.

Each one of us in our own way is challenged to open our own prison doors through love.

In Resonance Repatterning we gently identify the negative things we resonate with, and the positive things we need to resonate with. When we change our resonance, we feel lighter and in our own small way we find ourselves going into action to express the love that is within ourselves.

Love is always the common denominator of healing. There are different ways of getting there, but ultimately all healing is about becoming conscious of the unconditional love that is who we are – the creative principle that Starr Daily talks of.

But a friend insists, "What if your partner or child *still* doesn't hear your need and doesn't take out the trash, what then?"

A relationship of love is about supporting the basic underlying needs we all have. If you are in intimate partnership with someone and you love each other, you are already supporting one or more of the following needs:

- the need for giving support to each other on many levels and receiving support

- the need for financial and emotional security

- the need for sexual bonding and affection in intimate relationship

- the need for friendship, communication, humor and bonding of the heart through appreciation and respect

- the need for clear thinking and setting boundaries on negative or non-coherent behavior

- the need for shared spiritual values

In relationships that work best, we are aligned with each other and want to meet these needs in the give and take of relationship.

If important needs are not met and the inner work is not done to change the situation, the relationship doesn't usually last. Either it ends in separation or divorce or it ends through emotional distancing, withdrawal, upsets, anger and quarrels.

The heart closes down when basic needs are not met and we miss the opportunity to access the creative principle of unconditional love through relationship.

Remember, when needs are not met, the first step is to look at our own personal growth that is asking to be completed. What is the unmet need from our earlier experience that we still resonate with and superimpose on the present relationship? Until this resonance is identified and changed, frustration over needs in the present situation that aren't being met will continue.

Inner work to change our own resonance patterns supports us in reconnecting to our awareness of the creative principle of love. And from this place of unconditional love we communicate our needs – and our needs are met.

As with Starr Daily – as soon as he connected to the creative principle, the doctor couldn't stop himself from checking on his health, the guard couldn't stop himself from wanting to bring him food and the deputy warden couldn't stop himself from freeing him from the dungeon. All his needs were met without asking! This is the mystery of the creative principle of unconditional love.

FURTHER READING

Starr Daily. *Love Can Open Prison Doors.* London: Pernell and Sons, 1947, reprinted 1951.

4.

THE BLESSING OF ANGER REPATTERNING

THE BLESSING OF ANGER REPATTERNING

A. Read or tell the story about love can open prison doors *p.95*
Ask, "What does this story mean for you?" *[cr]with "I (*name the positive meaning*)" (*will be off/umb off*).

B. Identify the irritation or anger
Ask, "Who are you angry with? What are you angry about?"
*[cr] (*will be on/umb on because you resonate with diminishing your light through your impatience, irritation or anger*).

Understanding the irritation or anger
Explain: Any irritation, impatience or anger is a signal that your Wood Element wants some kind of positive change within yourself: some kind of inner growth. But anger disconnects your awareness from the creative principle of unconditional love for yourself and the person you are angry with.

The four steps in the downward spiral of anger {C–F}:

C. Step one – blame
Ask, "What do you blame (*name person*) for?"
*[cr] (*will be on/umb on because client resonates with blame*).

D. Step two – the judgments
Ask, "What judgments do you hear yourself making about (*name the person involved*)?"
*[cr] "(*Name the judgments about the person*)" (*will be on/umb on because client resonates with judgments rather than with benevolence, beyond right and wrong thinking*).

*[cr] with, "I (*name the same judgments client made about the other person*)" (*will be on/umb on because resonance with judgments about others is automatically superimposed on oneself*).

E. Step three – the dislike

*[**cr**] with, "I dislike (*name the person involved*) and myself" *(will be on/umb on)*.

F. Step four – the negative consequences or actions that result

Ask, "What is the result of your anger? What negative actions occur – conflict, verbal abuse, withdrawal, loss of caring or other negative action?" *[**cr**] *(will be on/umb on)*.

G. The creative principle used for non-coherent purposes

*[**cr**] with, "I use the creative principle of unconditional love to (blame myself • blame (*name person*) • go into negative judgments • dislike (*name person*) • dislike myself • quarrel • withdraw and cut off • justify why I am right and he/she is wrong • get into conflict • react with hypersensitivity • get sick • other negative action)" *(will be on/umb on because client resonates with using the creative principle of unconditional love for anger reactions)*.

The five steps for using the creative principle of unconditional love to make a quantum leap to a new way of being {H–L}:

H. Step 1: Awareness of the creative principle

Do {a–c} in sequence.

a. *Ask,* "In terms of the present situation and the possibilities for your own growth, what do you want to use the creative principle of unconditional love for?"
*[**cr**] with "I use the creative principle of unconditional love to (*name the positive that you want to use it for*)" *(will be off/umb off as client doesn't resonate with using the creative principle for constructive growth and positive change within him/herself)*.

b. *Ask*, "What do you love about (*name the person involved*)? What compassion do you feel for him/her?"
*[**cr**] with "I like/love that (*name love*) and I feel compassion for (*name person*) because (*name compassion*)" *(will be off/umb off because in this situation you do not yet resonate with love and compassion)*.

c. *Ask*, "What do you love about yourself? What compassion do you feel for yourself?"
*[**cr**] *(will be off/umb off because in this situation you do not yet resonate with love and compassion for yourself).*

I. Step 2: The underlying issue within self
Explain: The external situation is never the problem. The real problem is within our self – nothing to do with the other person/people involved. The problem situation is bringing up something that we need to look at within ourself.

Ask, "What change or growth do you imagine you need in relation to this situation?"
*[**cr**] with "I (*name the positive change that is needed*)" *(will be off/umb off because client does not resonate with the self-change).*

J. Step 3: Underneath every irritation is a underlying need that has not been expressed or met

Understanding the underlying need
Every problem – including the problem of impatience, irritation and anger – is associated with a need from your infancy and childhood that was not met.

When you are angry, this same unmet need from your past, with its hard wired neural pathways, is activated – and the past feelings and beliefs are superimposed on the present.

It is important to understand that the present unmet need stems from your childhood. If you don't resonate with the past need, it cannot be met in the present and you will keep repeating the pattern of your needs not being met.

Identify the underlying need from the following list. *Once you have identified the positive need* **that was not met in the past**, *observe how it relates to the present situation of anger.*

(**mcs**) {1–5} for the category; then (**mcs**) for the numbered item in that category.
*[**cr**] *(will be off/umb off because client doesn't yet resonate with the need).*

1. **The need for security and survival**
    (**mcs**) {1–9}.
    1. (I am cared for • I am looked after • My underlying needs are met).
    2. I feel secure.
    3. Everything is provided for.
    4. (I survive • I am successful).
    5. I am protected.
    6. I have a home.
    7. I am clothed, fed and kept warm.
    8. (I am welcomed • I belong).
    9. Other: *Ask,* "What do you need in order to feel secure about your survival?"

2. **Physical needs for health and energy**
    (**mcs**) {1–10}.
    1. I take in and appreciate living food (mother's milk • fresh homegrown fruits and vegetables • pure water).
    2. I breathe pure air.
    3. (I am warm • I receive the warmth of the sun).
    4. (I move for life • I am energized by movement).
    5. I sleep well and wake up refreshed.
    6. I receive all the (sunlight • full-spectrum light) I need.
    7. I do those actions that lead to health and energy.
    8. I think positive thoughts and feel good about myself and others.
    9. I relax and rejuvenate myself.
    10. Other: *Ask,* "What do you need for your health and energy?"

3. **The need to achieve your best, go beyond your limits and manifest your potential**
    (**mcs**) {1–13}. *[**cr**] (will be off/umb off).*
    1. (I achieve my best • I value those who help me achieve my best).

2. (I manifest my potential • I am successful • I enjoy going beyond the limits of what I thought was possible).
3. I have the strength and faith to persevere through obstacles and apparent failures.
4. I accept that achieving my dream has its ups and downs, involves hard work and brings its own hard knocks.
5. I serve (others • humanity).
6. I play (joyfully • spontaneously).
7. I am curious.
8. (I create beauty • I am creative in everything I do).
9. I am confident.
10. I am courageous.
11. I maintain an optimistic attitude no matter what difficulties I'm facing.
12. I put my concern for human well-being and right action before my need for (material success • the achievement of my ambitions).
13. Other: *Ask,* "What do you need that would allow you to manifest your potential, go beyond the limits of what you think is possible and achieve your best?"

4. **The need for love and respect in relationship**
    (**mcs**) {1–19}.
    1. I (receive love • give love • feel worthy of being loved) in my relationships.
    2. I have (close • affectionate • caring) relationships.
    3. I belong and feel (welcomed • included • wanted).
    4. I am enough.
    5. I make loving connections through warm and relaxed eye contact.
    6. I give and receive loving touch.
    7. I am protected from harm.
    8. (I have clear safe boundaries • I feel safe).
    9. I am (appreciated • acknowledged • valued • respected • accepted).
    10. I enjoy harmonious relationships.
    11. (I have positive communication in my relationship(s) • I am heard • I hear).

12. (I am seen • I see).
13. I freely express my (truth • feelings • thoughts • ideas • humor).
14. I (relax and laugh • enjoy humor).
15. I am free to explore and return for loving touch and bonding whenever I need to.
16. My heart is open to (compassion • understanding • love).
17. (I forgive • I am forgiven • I resolve problems and grow in my capacity to love).
18. I let go of (reactiveness • blame • complaints • feeling a victim • gossip).
19. Other: *Ask,* "What do you need that would bring you love and respect in your relationship(s)?"

5. **The need for meaning, purpose, love, and happiness from within (mcs)** {1–24}. *[**cr**] *(will be off/umb off)*.
   1. (I feel joyful • I let go of all negative thoughts and tune in to love).
   2. I am filled with gratitude every day.
   3. I persevere with focused attention.
   4. I commit myself 100%. I name my goal with confidence, no matter what others think.
   5. I appreciate the synchronous events that let me know I am going in the right direction.
   6. I am openhearted and friendly, and divine help comes to me naturally through the help of others.
   7. (I see beauty • I see the Divine) in every aspect of the creation.
   8. I am content.
   9. (I have faith • I trust that every experience is for my highest good).
   10. I am (focused • disciplined).
   11. (I pay attention to my thoughts and the stillness of my mind • I am still).
   12. I accept the divine will, free of resistance and fear.
   13. I let go. I get out of the way and let God.
   14. I live my (truth • values) in action.

15. I love unconditionally.
16. (I stand for what is right • I live with integrity).
17. (I practice the presence of God • I feel spiritually connected at all times to the Divine within).
18. I let go of (self-importance • negative thoughts and feelings).
19. (I am at peace • My mind is peaceful).
20. (I am receptive to divine grace).
21. (I serve selflessly • I give generously • I find every opportunity to help others).
22. I stay conscious of the light within and the light within each person I meet.
23. I am receptive to the higher purpose and meaning of every circumstance life brings.
24. I let go of my need to get (upset • angry • worried) about anything in this world. I trust. I have faith.

K. Step 4: The positive habit or action needed for reconnecting to the creative principle of love in this situation

Do {a–b) in sequence.

a. *[cr] with "I immediately stop myself from thinking or talking negatively about (*name person*) and harming both him/her and myself in this way" *(will be off/umb off)*.

b. *Ask*, "What positive habit or action do you need to integrate and do that will help you reconnect to the creative principle of love in this situation?" *[cr] *(will be off/umb off)*.

L. Step 5: The three communications

Do {1–3} in sequence. It is best to do Step 5 in a session rather than doing it with the person involved. Once the resonance has shifted, client may find him/herself integrating the three communications quite naturally into challenging situations.

1. **State the fact of what you observe to (*name person*) free of blame or judgments**
    Ask, "What is the actual fact of the situation? How can you communicate this fact free of all blame and judgments?"

    Practitioner states, "We are checking your resonance with communicating free of blame or judgments with (*name person*)." Practitioner represents the person involved for this communication.

    *[**cr**] with "I notice that you (*name the fact of what you notice in a present tense statement*)" *(will be off/umb off because client does not resonate with* **communicating** *the facts free of blame, judgments or an emotional charge).*

2. **Communicate the underlying feeling beneath the anger to (*name person*)**
    Ask, "What is your **real** feeling about this fact?"
    Explain: The real feeling is not about feeling angry: it is usually a feeling relating to something you aren't getting or something you need that isn't being fulfilled for you.

    Practitioner states, "We are checking your resonance with communicating your real feeling beneath the anger to (*name person*)." Practitioner represents the person involved for this communication.
    *[**cr**] with "I feel (*name the feeling*)" *(will be off/umb off because client doesn't resonate with* **communicating** *the real feeling to person involved).*

3. **Share the real need and the positive feeling of having your need met**
    Ask, "What is your **real** need and what is the positive feeling you have when this real need is met?"

    Practitioner states, "We are checking your resonance with communicating your real need and the positive feeling of having your need met with (*name person*)." Practitioner represents the person involved for this communication.

*[**cr**] with "I need (*name the need*) and when you (*name the need*), I feel (*name the positive feelings*)" (*will be off/umb off because you do not resonate with communicating your real need and the positive feeling*).

M. The Wood Element coherence that supports connection to the creative principle of love

*[**cr**] with "I am ready for new beginnings with (*name person*) and with hope, optimism and positive action I move forward in my personal growth towards my highest potential for experiencing unconditional love" (*will be off/umb off because at the moment client does not resonate with this level of Wood Element balance and harmony*).

N. Identify the Energizing Option needed

(**mcs**) for the Energizing Option from the SPIRAL UP! book that is needed for shifting the resonance patterns identified in this Repatterning.

If you are a Resonance Repatterning practitioner, you will then recheck the *[**cr**] statements to confirm the change.

HOW TO USE THE BLESSING OF ANGER REPATTERING IN YOUR DAILY LIFE
EVEN IF YOU HAVE NOT YET ATTENDED A RESONANCE REPATTERING SEMINAR

- Observe when you go into the four steps of the downward spiral of anger: blame, judgments, dislike and negative actions. Recognize that you have a choice to stop this downward spiral and tune in to the creative principle.

- When in an angry situation, take a pause. Give yourself and the other person space. Say that you need to calm down and do some clear thinking. Then get in touch with the five steps for using the creative principle of love.

- You may want to take just one or two letters of the Repattering – {B} and {C} for instance and then do an Energizing Option to change your resonance with the letters you have identified.

- Gradually you can do different combinations of letters in relation to the same problem.

  When you do different combinations like this, your negative resonance with the problem may still keep showing up because you are getting in touch with specific aspects of the overall problem in the other letters – {D}, {E} and so on. In this way you are in your process of positive change in a combination of ways.

RR SESSIONS: *If you would like to receive the complete Repattering with a professional Resonance Repattering Practitioner, in person or over the phone, go to ResonanceRepattering.net > Sessions for RR Institute Practitioners worldwide who have listed themselves on the RRI website.*

RR SEMINARS: *If you would like to attend Resonance Repattering seminars in person or online, so you can use RR effectively on yourself and/or others, go to ResonanceRepattering.net > Seminars for the list of teachers endorsed by the Resonance Repattering Institute to teach.*

5. TURN YOUR FEAR
INTO COURAGE

In 1940, World War II, Britain was in her darkest hour. Most of Europe was either overrun by the Nazis or had aligned with Germany. France had fallen; Russia and Italy were aligned with Hitler. Britain and the commonwealth countries, with few resources and no powerful allies, were alone, and Hitler's invasion of England was imminent. The USA did not enter the war for two more years. Churchill was aware of the oncoming destruction to be faced, but at the same time he held firm to his vision that this would be Britain's finest hour. He held the polarity of these two opposites in his vision and at the same time spurred the nation to courage and power:

> We shall defend our island, whatever the cost may be. We shall fight on the beaches. We shall fight on the landing grounds. We shall fight in the fields and in the streets. We shall fight in the hills. We shall never surrender. Let us brace ourselves to do our duties, and so bear ourselves that, if the British Empire and Commonwealth last for a thousand years, men will say, 'This was their finest hour.'
>
> Winston Churchill quoted in Margaret Gaskin's
> *Blitz: The Story of December 29, 1940*

FEAR TO COURAGE IN DIFFICULT SITUATIONS

What is it that makes people courageous in the face of disaster?
- Like the old lady – two gunmen facing her – who put her fingers onto the gun barrels and said, "Let's sit down and talk."

- Or Helen Keller – deaf, blind, unable to speak, living in a dark world – who would write, "Life is a daring adventure or nothing."

- Or, after an intense three-hour blitz in 1940, London in flames after 400 high-explosive bombs had been dropped plus 22,000 lethal incendiaries – people were back at work the next day, climbing over the rubble, Fleet Street newspapers were being delivered, and a chambermaid seriously commented to an American journalist, "Well, I'll never forgive that old Hitler if he bombs us on Christmas Day!"

People in situations of total disaster have somehow managed to turn their fear into courage and they become an example and inspiration for us as we face our own daily fears.

～

In *"Turn Your Fear into Courage,"* we'll look at what we do that feeds our fears, and equally what we do that feeds our courage. We'll understand that fear has its purpose and how fear is an invitation to each one of us to live in tune with our inner strengths – our light.

If we want to understand what supports us in being powerful and courageous in the face of our fears, we first need to look at what fear is about: what are the different kinds of fears we face, and what are the acts of courage that neutralize our fears?

Fear from three perspectives

1. The physiological aspect: what happens on the physical level when we are afraid – our brain-body neural pathways

2. Dr. Edward Bach's point of view: the five flower essences for five kinds of fear

3. The Five Element Acupuncture point of view: the fears associated with the Five Elements

How fear relates to our brain-body neural pathways

Let's start with how fear relates to our physiology. Whenever we are afraid, there are five aspects we need to understand if we want to neutralize our fear on the physical level:

1. Our fear activates a sympathetic nervous system (SNS) adrenaline stress response and we immediately go into an alert fight or flight reaction. Our ability to respond in this way helps us survive dangers and threatening situations.

2. Any SNS stress response in the present always relates to an alert fight-flight stress response from our past when we either succeeded in fighting or running away from a danger or we didn't. If we didn't overcome or run away from a threatening situation, we move into chronic fear (or anger, sadness, loss of joy, etc.). If we succeeded in overcoming or running away from a danger, we create positive neural pathways for success and courage.

3. When the needs of a baby, infant or child for safety, protection and love etc., are not met, it feels like a life-or-death situation for the infant or child. And in fact it may be a life-and-death trauma. As a result of feeling so threatened, our frequencies move out of sync and we begin to resonate with chronic fear – not just a temporary response to a threatening situation.

4. When a present situation even slightly resembles the past situation, it activates the same feeling of life or death, which triggers the same cascade of stress neurochemicals and fires the same adrenaline fight-flight nerve pathways. Every time we indulge in negative thoughts or fearful, angry, anxious feeling reactions, we continue to reactivate and strengthen these stress pathways in the brain and body. Finally, as a result of constant use, these neural pathways become hardwired and automatic.

    In Resonance Repatterning sessions that we do on ourselves or receive, we change our resonance with negative thought patterns and highly charged feelings. As a result, we interrupt the nerve pathways and cascade of stress neurochemicals that create our distress in the present.

In the past, especially as infants and small children, we couldn't get all our needs met. Now in the present it is different. We can get our needs met. By actively resonating with new and positive beliefs, needs and feelings, and resonating with knowing our needs, communicating them and meeting them, we create new nerve pathways. And sooner or later the old pathways atrophy from lack of use.

5. When something upsetting happens in the present, we have about two seconds before we activate the old automatic, hardwired brain-body pathways. And we have about two seconds to activate new and positive pathways and neural connections instead of the old ones. Each time we take control in this way and refuse to fire the old stress pathways, they become weaker and weaker. Later, in the **Fear to Courage Repatterning** that follows, we'll look at what we can do in those two seconds to activate new empowering pathways.

The five Flower Essence fears

Dr. Edward Bach was a medical doctor who, in 1930, began to develop a natural form of medicine based on flower essences. Bach talks about five kinds of fear that are related to five different flower essences: Aspen, Mimulus, Red Chestnut, Cherry Plum and Rock Rose. Knowing these five essences may help us gain a deeper understanding of the different kinds of fear we go into and how we can free ourselves of these fears.

1. **An Aspen fear** is a vague unexplainable fear that has no reason or cause. People suffering from Aspen fear are afraid to share their fear with others because there is no reason for their fear – it feels illogical.

2. **A Mimulus fear** is a fear of a known cause – such as fear of the dark, poverty, loss of a job, public opinion, illness, spiders, public speaking, not having enough food in the fridge, having electricity and water cut off, and so on.

3. **A Red Chestnut fear** involves fears for other people, for loved ones or friends, that something unfortunate will happen to them.

4. **A Cherry Plum fear** is a fear of the mind and reason giving way. There is a fear of doing something dreadful – especially hurting oneself or someone else.

5. Finally there is **a Rock Rose fear**, which is a fear as a result of an accident, sudden illness or shock when the individual is very frightened or even terrified.

In the Fear to Courage Repatterning, we will look at these five fears in relation to the flower essences and the courage that is also related to each of these five flower essences.

The fears associated with the Five Elements of Chinese Acupuncture

We can also look at fear energetically, from the point of view of the Five Elements of ancient Chinese Acupuncture.

The Five Elements of Wood, Fire, Earth, Metal and Water form a universal map for understanding frequencies and how we can live a long and healthy life by balancing the energy in these Five Elements. Each of the five Elements gives us an understanding about our fears and the courage that each Element provides for transcending our fears.

The Wood Element

When our Wood Element is off balance, we might be afraid of new beginnings – a new job, a new date, meeting new people, being in new situations. It might also cause us to be afraid of being self-assertive, of standing up for ourselves and others or standing up for what we know is right.

WOOD ELEMENT COURAGE STORY

The courage related to the Wood Element comes from its quality of hope and self-esteem. However dark and hopeless the present situation, there is always some kind of action we can do that will lead us step by step towards our vision and what we want.

In WWII a London cab driver, questioned by an American correspondent on the fall of France to the Nazis, exemplifies this kind of Wood courage of hope and self-assertion in the face of fear. Britain was now alone, with no powerful allies, was close to bankruptcy and had very little food and resources. The reporter asked the cab driver, did he think Britain could really beat Hitler alone? "Well," the cockney cabbie replied, almost cheerily, "we can't if we don't try, can we, guv'nor?"

This is the Wood Element for you: there's always hope as long as you go into action and try! Or the cockney lady handling the elevator who commented to the same journalist about the fall of France to the Nazis, "Well sir, things are looking up! There's no one else to let us down."

⁓

A strong, optimistic Wood Element sees the glass as half-full, never as half-empty. It always provides a hopeful vision of things. For instance, the stock market and the economy always go up and down. But if you look at a graph for the last eighty years, stocks inevitably spike higher and higher, no matter how many times they drop or how far they drop. A finance planner commented that "The downs are good because they make you re-evaluate your business and your values. In down times you see your weak areas and do something about them. This prepares you so you are ready for the upswing that always follows every downswing."

Again, this is strong Wood energy: go into action in down times – prepare yourself for the future you want, fight for it, clean out the dead wood and get ready for the upswing.

Sometimes all we can do is ride out the low times without collapsing. People have always managed to do this – whether in wars or concentration camps, natural disasters or economic depressions. The strength of the Wood Element helps us keep our vision and our actions aligned to our goals so we are always ready for the upswing when it comes.

The Fire Element

When our Fire Element is off balance, we may be afraid of intimacy and sexuality and have a fear about our safety, feeling vulnerable and unprotected. We may also have fears about being controlled or losing control, or fears of social situations and communication.

FIRE ELEMENT COURAGE STORY

The courage related to the Fire Element comes from its quality of humor. In *Blitz* by Margaret Gaskin, she gives many examples of people responding with humor in life death situations.

For instance, during the Blitz, London was divided into Reporting Posts. A group of unarmed volunteers were responsible for each Post, getting the people living in that area to shelter in the underground subways. One Post put up the following Monty Python-type notice: "If this Post is attacked, it will resist by every means and remain until relieved. If the garrison cannot remain alive it will remain dead – but in any case IT WILL REMAIN!"

The Earth Element

When the Earth Element is off balance, it may cause us to have fears about our survival: will I have food, water, a roof over my head, clothing, etc.? It could also show up as a fear that we won't be supported.

EARTH ELEMENT COURAGE STORY

The courage related to the Earth Element is about helping other people. A business training coach – Brian Tracy – says, "Successful people are always looking for opportunities to help others. Unsuccessful people are always asking, 'What's in it for me?'" This is one of the great ways of turning fear into courage through our Earth Element: keep helping others, no matter what is happening.

There were many moving examples of this during the crisis of the Japanese nuclear leak and tsunami: people would return home to find that some unknown person had left food for them on their doorstep.

And in Washington D.C., when a Boeing 707 with ice on its wings flew into the Potomac River, one vision was etched in everyone's mind: the sight of an unknown hand, pushing survivors out of the hatch in the back of the plane to the surface of the frozen water and to safety. Finally the hand disappeared. He sacrificed himself to save others. This is the ultimate sacrifice of the Earth Element person – such a sense of empathy for others' suffering and a desire to help, that he/she puts others' needs first.

The Metal Element

When our Metal Element is off balance, it may cause us to be afraid of failure, humiliation and embarrassment – even a fear of success. Another Metal fear is the fear of not being respected, the fear that we will never be part of the in-group, the VIPs or the top management. The fear of loss – whether of material objects, money, health or a marriage – is also a Metal fear. And the fear of being disconnected from the Divine.

The fear of humiliation and embarrassment is a big fear that most of us may not be aware we have. This fear of embarrassment stops us from being spontaneous, from following our bliss, as Joseph Campbell called it.

METAL ELEMENT COURAGE: SHAY'S STORY

The courage of the Metal Element involves doing what is right, putting human needs first before the need to win and compete to be best. Metal Element courage is about values – living our truth through right action.

There is a wonderful story about Metal Element courage – the power of doing what is right. The father of a handicapped child called Shay was giving the keynote speech at a fundraising dinner for a school that serves the learning disabled. He told a story about Shay that is unforgettable:

"Shay and I once walked past a park where some boys Shay knew were playing baseball. Shay asked, 'Do you think they'll let me play?' I knew that most of the boys would not want someone like Shay on their team, but I also understood that if Shay were allowed to play, it would give him a much-needed sense of belonging, to be accepted by others in spite of his handicaps."

Here we see the father's strong Metal Element: he could have been embarrassed for Shay, that Shay would be humiliated trying to play with the other boys. Or he might have been embarrassed for himself and suggested that they go home and play together. Instead he heard Shay's need to play with the boys and had the courage to find out if that need could be met.

The father continued his speech: "I approached one of the boys on the field and asked if Shay could play, not expecting much. The boy looked around for guidance and said, 'We're losing by six runs and the game is in the eighth inning. I guess he can be on our team and we'll try to put him in to bat in the ninth inning.'

"Shay struggled over to the team's bench, put on a team shirt with a broad smile. I had a small tear in my eye and warmth in my heart. The boys saw my joy at Shay's being accepted.

"In the bottom of the eighth inning, Shay's team scored a few runs but was still behind by three.... In the bottom of the ninth inning, Shay's team scored again. Now, with two outs and the bases loaded, the potential winning run was on base and Shay was scheduled to be next at bat.

"At this juncture, do they let Shay bat and give away their chance to win the game? Surprisingly, Shay was given the bat. Everyone knew that a hit was all but impossible because Shay didn't even know how to hold the bat properly, much less connect with the ball.

"However, as Shay stepped up to the plate the pitcher, recognizing that the other team was putting winning aside for this moment in Shay's life, moved in a few steps to lob the ball in softly so Shay would at least be able to make contact. The first pitch came and Shay swung clumsily and missed. The pitcher again took a few steps forward to toss the ball softly towards Shay. As the pitch came in, Shay swung at the ball and hit a slow ground ball right back to the pitcher.

"The game would now be over; the pitcher picked up the soft grounder and could have easily thrown the ball to the first baseman. Shay would have been out and that would have been the end of the game. Instead the pitcher threw the ball right over the head of the first baseman, out of reach of all his teammates.

"Everyone from the stands and both teams started yelling, 'Shay, run to first! Run to first!' Never in his life had Shay ever run that far but he made it to first base. He scampered down the baseline, wide-eyed and startled. Everyone yelled, 'Run to second, run to second!'

"Catching his breath, Shay awkwardly ran towards second, gleaming and struggling to make it to second base.... Now the right fielder had the ball. He could have thrown the ball to the second baseman for the tag, but he understood the pitcher's intentions and he too intentionally threw the ball high and far over the third baseman's head. Shay ran toward third base deliriously as the runners ahead of him circled the bases toward home.
All were screaming, 'Shay, Shay, Shay, all the way, Shay!'

"The opposing shortstop ran to help Shay and shouted, 'Run home, Shay, run to home!' As Shay started running, the boys from both teams and those watching were on their feet screaming, 'Shay, run home!' Shay ran to home, stepped on the plate and was cheered as the hero who hit the 'grand slam' and won the game for his team.

"That day, with tears now rolling down my face, the boys from both teams helped bring a piece of true love and humanity into this world.

"Shay didn't make it to another summer; he died that winter, having never forgotten being the hero of the game."

This is Metal Element courage: the authentic action; doing what is true and right in action. Shay's father took the first step; the small boy continued by letting Shay bat; the pitcher took the baton and passed it to the right fielder; and both teams and the people watching caught the spirit that something was happening here that was bigger than all of them – a peak moment they would remember for the rest of their lives.

The Water Element

Water is the Element **directly related to fear**. But we must remember that the Water Element is also associated with **power, energy and courage**. When we have a strong, balanced Water Element energy:

- it gives us the courage and calmness to face whatever is put before us in life

- it gives us the clarity to see beyond our fears

- it gives us the willpower, energy and drive to keep persevering around all obstacles – regardless of our fears

WATER ELEMENT COURAGE STORY

Sometimes moving through our fear with courage may involve a quite simple everyday challenge. For instance, I remember once dancing the Viennese Waltz with my dance teacher. Graceful as this dance is, it is also very fast and involves constant rotation. At one point the heel of my shoe became caught inside my other shoe and I fell straight backwards like a felled tree! Fortunately my teacher buffered my fall so I wasn't hurt, but I was quite shaken and naturally I wanted to sit out for the rest of the class. Fear!

My teacher would have none of it. He insisted that I get up and continue dancing. "Well, let's do it slowly," I said. "No," he replied, "Up to speed." "Well then, let's do it without music," I pleaded. "No, with music!" My teacher refused to let me reinforce the old fear pathway by not dancing. He immediately had me strengthen the pathway of joy by continuing to dance – this time free of falling! He empowered my Water Element courage – and I was able to keep moving.

$\backsim$

FURTHER READING

Margaret Gaskin. *Blitz: The Story of December 29, 1940*. London: Harcourt, 2005.

Bach Flower Essences for the Family. Oxfordshire: Wigmore Publications, 1993.

Philip M. Chancellor. *Handbook of the Bach Flower Remedies*. London: C.W. Daniel, 1971.

Chloe Faith Wordsworth. *Inner Cultivation through the Twelve Meridians: The Five Essences*. Scottsdale, AZ: Resonance Publishing, 2004, 2016.

5.

FEAR TO COURAGE
REPATTERNING

FEAR TO COURAGE REPATTERNING

A. Read fear to courage in difficult situations *p.105*

Ask, "What does this story mean for you?" *[**cr**]with "I (*name the positive meaning*)" *(will be off/umb off)*.

B. Name the fears in the current situation

Ask, "What are you afraid of – perhaps in terms of your work life, your home life, security fears – whatever fear comes to your mind?"

*[**cr**] with, "I am afraid (*name the fears*)" *(will be on/umb on)*.

C. Identify the Bach Flower Essence fear involved

(**mcs**) {a–e} for the Flower Essence fear(s) involved.

a. Aspen fear: fears and anxiety of an unknown origin

(**mcs**) {1–5}. *[**cr**] *(will be on/umb on)*.

1. I am suddenly afraid for no specific reason.
2. I am nervy and anxious.
3. I wake up in fear or terror from a bad dream, sometimes trembling and sweating.
4. I am hypersensitive and over-imaginative and go into a paralyzing terror.
5. I am afraid of confiding in others about my fears because there is no reason for them.

b. Mimulus fear: fear of known things

(**mcs**) {1–5}. *[**cr**] *(will be on/umb on)*.

1. I am afraid of (illness • death • accidents • the dark • violence • growing old • other – *Ask:* What is the known thing you are afraid of?).
2. I am shy and retiring and become tongue-tied around people.
3. I tend to blush or laugh nervously.
4. I hide my fears.
5. I am afraid of natural disasters.

c. **Red Chestnut fear: fear for others**
(**mcs**) {1–5}. *[**cr**] *(will be on/umb on)*.
   1. I fear the worst for my loved ones.
   2. I turn (*someone's/name person*)'s minor complaint into a major problem.
   3. I worry about other people's problems.
   4. Because of my fears, I tend to force my (help • solutions) onto others.
   5. (If someone is late, I fear the worst • If someone goes on holiday, I am afraid something bad will happen to them).

d. **Cherry Plum fear: fear of the mind giving way and breaking down**
(**mcs**) {1–6}. *[**cr**] *(will be on/umb on)*.
   1. I feel depressed.
   2. I am in despair.
   3. I am afraid of losing my sanity.
   4. I am highly strung and afraid I could go into a hasty action and hurt myself or someone else.
   5. I am afraid of (my violent impulses • being abusive to myself/others).
   6. I explode in sudden outbursts of rage.

e. **Rock Rose fear: terror**
(**mcs**) {1–4}. *[**cr**] *(will be on/umb on)*.
   1. I am frozen with fear after (a natural disaster • sudden illness • a mugging • an accident • witnessing an accident • abuse • experiencing violence).
   2. I feel helpless and terrified in the face of (a natural disaster • sudden illness • a mugging • an accident • witnessing an accident • abuse).
   3. (I have night terrors • I experience sheer terror).
   4. I become exhausted from long-term terror.

D. **Identify the Five Elements fear involved**
(**mcs**) {1–5} for the Element involved.
   1. **Wood Element**
      (**mcs**) {1–2}. *[**cr**] *(will be on/umb on)*.

1. I am afraid of (change • new beginnings • a new job • a new date • a new situation).
2. I am afraid to be self-assertive and go into action for what I want.

2. **Fire Element**
   (**mcs**) {1–4}. *[**cr**] (will be on/umb on).
   1. I am afraid of (intimacy • sexuality)
   2. I am afraid of being unsafe and unprotected.
   3. I am afraid of social situations.
   4. I have a fear of communicating.

3. **Earth Element**
   (**mcs**) {1–4}. *[**cr**] (will be on/umb on).
   1. I am afraid I can't survive.
   2. I am afraid I won't have (food • water • a roof over my head • clothing • the ability to support myself).
   3. I am afraid of being homeless.
   4. I am afraid I won't be supported.

4. **Metal Element**
   (**mcs**) {1–6}. *[**cr**] (will be on/umb on).
   1. I am afraid of (failure • humiliation • embarrassment).
   2. I am afraid of being disrespected.
   3. I am afraid of losing (my money • my health • my home • other).
   4. I am afraid of (God • of displeasing God • being cut off from God).
   5. (I am self-conscious • I avoid being spontaneous so I don't make a fool of myself).
   6. I am afraid (to trust in God • of surrendering to the divine will for me and my life).

5. **Water Element**
   (**mcs**) {1–5}. *[**cr**] (will be on/umb on).
   1. My fear disempowers me and (I give up • I no longer persevere to achieve my goal/vision).
   2. I feel unclear and confused with fear.

3. (I feel terrified • I go into a panic • I freeze with fear).
4. My fears deplete my energy reserves and I feel exhausted.
5. I don't use my willpower to overcome my fears.

E. Identify the chronic SNS stress response involved

(**mcs**) (1–3) for the stress response involved with the fears.

1. **The non-coherent *alert* response neural pathway being reactivated in the present situation that (*name client*) still resonates with because of unresolved fears from the past**
   (**mcs**) {1–7}. *[**cr**] (*will be on/umb on*).
   1. (I freeze • I am incapable of action • I am paralyzed).
   2. I am inappropriately triggered into a hyper-aroused state.
   3. I (hide • isolate myself) because life is so dangerous.
   4. I am startled by (small things • anything).
   5. I can't relax because I can't (see who or what is dangerous • locate the source of a danger).
   6. I am on the alert for danger all the time.
   7. I am tense all the time.

2. **The non-coherent *fight* response neural pathway client still resonates with in an attempt to discharge the unresolved fears from the past**
   (**mcs**) {1–12}. *[**cr**] (*will be on/umb on*).
   1. (I am defensive • I overreact).
   2. I am overly assertive.
   3. (I am quarrelsome • I pick quarrels).
   4. I am (impatient • angry • frustrated • enraged).
   5. I easily become violent.
   6. I am (hyper-nervous • hyper-sensitive • high strung).
   7. I am a caretaker for everyone.
   8. I am (over-controlling • dominating).
   9. (I am excessively talkative • I interrupt (*name person/others*) before he/she/they has/have finished talking).
   10. (I make others wrong • I tell (*name person*) that he/she is wrong).
   11. I use sex to discharge my anger.
   12. I can't keep still.

3. **The non-coherent** *flight* **response neural pathway client still resonates with because of the unresolved fears from the past**
   (**mcs**) {1–9}. *[**cr**] *(will be on/umb on)*.
   1. (I am unable to avoid dangerous situations • I habitually put myself in dangerous situations).
   2. I run away from situations in a panic, unable to think clearly.
   3. (I get in a panic • I am chronically anxious).
   4. I turn to (food • alcohol • drugs • cigarettes • sex • sleep • day-dreaming • reading/movies • gambling • other) as a way to escape my fears.
   5. (I become ill as a way to avoid a threatening situation • I run away from life).
   6. I stop (hearing • seeing • tasting • smelling • feeling).
   7. I escape my fears by being depressed.
   8. (I can't get going • I can't move into action • I can't (run away from • avoid) danger).
   9. I cry as a way of handling any emotionally charged situation I can't cope with.

F. **Identify the earlier experience associated with the fears**
   Ask, "What earlier experience do you feel is associated with your fears?"
   *[**cr**] *(will be on/umb on)*.

G. **Identify the underlying need that was not met in the past, which (*Client*) needs to resonate with in the present in order to create new neural pathways for courage and to neutralize the fear pathways**
   (**mcs**) (1–5) for the underlying need category involved.
   1. **The need for security and survival**
      (**mcs**) {1–9}. *[**cr**] *(will be off/umb off)*.
      1. (I am cared for • I am looked after • My underlying needs are met).
      2. I feel secure.
      3. Everything is provided for.
      4. (I survive • I am successful).
      5. I am protected.
      6. I have a home.

7. I am clothed, fed and kept warm.
8. (I am welcomed • I belong).
9. Other: *Ask,* "What do you need in order to feel secure about your survival?"

2. **Physical needs for health and energy**
   (**mcs**) {1–10}. *[**cr**] *(will be off/umb off).*
   1. I take in and appreciate living food (mother's milk • fresh homegrown fruits and vegetables • pure water).
   2. I breathe pure air.
   3. (I am warm • I receive the warmth of the sun).
   4. (I move for life • I am energized by movement).
   5. I sleep well and wake up refreshed.
   6. I receive all the (sunlight • full-spectrum light) I need.
   7. I do those actions that lead to health and energy.
   8. I think positive thoughts and feel good about myself and others.
   9. I relax and rejuvenate myself.
   10. Other: *Ask,* "What do you need for your health and energy?"

3. **The need for love and respect in relationship**
   (**mcs**) {1–19}. *[**cr**] *(will be off/umb off).*
   1. I (receive love • give love • feel worthy of being loved) in my relationships.
   2. I have (close • affectionate • caring) relationships.
   3. I belong and feel (welcomed • included • wanted).
   4. I am enough.
   5. I make loving connections through warm and relaxed eye contact.
   6. I give and receive loving touch.
   7. I am protected from harm.
   8. I have clear safe boundaries • I feel safe.
   9. I am (appreciated • acknowledged • valued • respected • accepted).
   10. I enjoy harmonious relationships.
   11. (I have positive communication in my relationship(s) • I am heard • I hear).
   12. (I am seen • I see).

13. I freely express my (truth • feelings • thoughts • ideas • humor).
14. I (relax and laugh • enjoy humor).
15. I am free to explore and return for loving touch and bonding whenever I need to.
16. My heart is open to (compassion • understanding • love).
17. (I forgive • I am forgiven • I resolve problems and grow in my capacity to love).
18. I let go of (reactiveness • blame • complaints • feeling a victim • gossip).
19. Other: *Ask,* "What do you need that would bring you love and respect in your relationship(s)?"

4. **The need to achieve your best, go beyond your limits and manifest your potential**
(**mcs**) {1–13}. *[**cr**] *(will be off/umb off).*
1. (I achieve my best • I value those who help me achieve my best).
2. (I manifest my potential • I am successful • I enjoy going beyond the limits of what I thought was possible).
3. I have the strength and faith to persevere through obstacles and apparent failures.
4. I accept that achieving my dream has its ups and downs, involves hard work and brings its own hard knocks.
5. I serve (others • humanity).
6. I play (joyfully • spontaneously).
7. I am curious.
8. (I create beauty • I am creative in everything I do).
9. I am confident.
10. I am courageous.
11. I maintain an optimistic attitude no matter what difficulties I'm facing.
12. I put my concern for human well-being and right action before my need for (material success • the achievement of my ambitions).
13. Other: *Ask,* "What do you need that would allow you to manifest your potential, go beyond the limits of what you think is possible and achieve your best?"

5. **The need for meaning, purpose, love, and happiness from within** (**mcs**) {1–24}. *[**cr**] *(will be off/umb off).*
   1. (I feel joyful • I let go of all negative thoughts and tune in to love).
   2. I am filled with gratitude every day.
   3. I persevere with focused attention.
   4. I commit myself 100%. I name my goal with confidence, no matter what others think.
   5. I appreciate the synchronous events that let me know I am going in the right direction.
   6. I am openhearted and friendly, and divine help comes to me naturally through the help of others.
   7. (I see beauty • I see the Divine) in every aspect of the creation.
   8. I am content.
   9. (I have faith • I trust that every experience is for my highest good).
   10. I am (focused • disciplined).
   11. (I pay attention to my thoughts and the stillness of my mind • I am still).
   12. I accept the divine will, free of resistance and fear.
   13. I let go. I get out of the way and let God.
   14. I live my (truth • values) in action.
   15. I love unconditionally.
   16. (I stand for what is right • I live with integrity).
   17. (I practice the presence of God • I feel spiritually connected at all times to the Divine within).
   18. I let go of (self-importance • negative thoughts and feelings).
   19. (I am at peace • My mind is peaceful).
   20. (I am receptive to divine grace).
   21. (I serve selflessly • I give generously • I find every opportunity to help others).
   22. I stay conscious of the light within and the light within each person I meet.
   23. I am receptive to the higher purpose and meaning of every circumstance life brings.
   24. I let go of my need to get (upset • angry • worried) about anything in this world. I trust. I have faith.

H. Identify the coherent Bach Flower Essence needed for neutralizing fears with courage

(**mcs**) {a–e} for the Flower Essence(s) needed.

a. Coherent Aspen courage is needed for fears and anxiety of an unknown origin
(**mcs**) {1–4}. *[**cr**] *(will be off/umb off)*.
1. I have an inner confidence.
2. I enjoy adventure and new experiences.
3. I experience the joy of life, the joy of death and the joy of love.
4. I can move through any danger and difficulty unafraid because I am supported by love.

b. Coherent Mimulus courage is needed for fear of known things
(**mcs**) {1–6}. *[**cr**] *(will be off/umb off)*.
1. I have a quiet courage that allows me to face my trials with humor and confidence.
2. I stand up for myself.
3. I get my negative emotions under control and enjoy my life free of fear.
4. I know when I need to withdraw and be alone.
5. I accept what is, trusting that I have the courage to handle what life gives me.
6. I use my willpower to stop my negative thoughts concerning my fear of (*name the know fear*).

c. Coherent Red Chestnut courage is needed for fear for others
(**mcs**) {1–6}. *[**cr**] *(will be off/umb off)*.
1. I care for my loved ones with compassion and positive thoughts.
2. I radiate positive thoughts and health to all.
3. I am calm even in an emergency.
4. I give help when asked.
5. I have faith that others are being looked after.
6. I use my willpower to stop my negative thoughts concerning my fears for (*name person*/others).

d. **Coherent Cherry Plum courage is needed for fear of the mind giving way and breaking down**
(**mcs**) {1–4}. *[**cr**] *(will be off/umb off)*.
   1. I have a calm, quiet inner strength.
   2. I maintain my (equilibrium • balance • sanity) through extreme conditions.
   3. I come to terms with and resolve my inner conflicts.
   4. I am receptive to positive and wise guidance.

e. **Coherent Rock Rose courage is needed for terror**
(**mcs**) {1–5}. *[**cr**] *(will be off/umb off)*.
   1. I have great courage and presence of mind.
   2. I am willing to risk my own life in order to help as many people as possible.
   3. I have a strong will and character.
   4. In an emergency I am calm and give myself fully to aid others in their time of great need.
   5. (I am taken care of • I am guided from within • I trust and have faith in the higher power • I trust that only what is for my higher learning will happen).

I. **Identify the coherent Five Elements quality needed for neutralizing fear with courage**
(**mcs**) {a–e} for the Element involved.
   a. **Wood Element**
      (**mcs**) {1–2}. *[**cr**] *(will be off/umb off)*.
      1. I am always hopeful no matter what.
      2. I go into assertive action to do what is right and achieve a vision that works for all.

      Read the Wood Element courage story p.109
      Ask, "What does this story mean for you?" *[**cr**]with "I *(name the positive meaning)*" *(will be off/umb off)*.

b. **Fire Element**

(**mcs**) {1–3}. *[**cr**] (*will be off/umb off*).

1. I rise above my fear through humor and help others relax and laugh.
2. I laugh in the face of my fears.
3. I transcend my fears and help others rise above their fears by talking and listening.

Read the Fire Element courage story p.110
Ask, "What does this story mean for you?" *[**cr**]with "I (*name the positive meaning*)" (*will be off/umb off*).

c. **Earth Element**

(**mcs**) {1–5}. *[**cr**] (*will be off/umb off*).

1. I help others in every situation.
2. I support others in their time of need.
3. (I am looked after • My basic needs are met).
4. People are always there to give a helping hand in times of need.
5. I create a home wherever I am.

Read the Earth Element courage story p.111
Ask, "What does this story mean for you?" *[**cr**]with "I (*name the positive meaning*)" (*will be off/umb off*).

d. **Metal Element**

(**mcs**) {1–5}. *[**cr**] (*will be off/umb off*).

1. I do right action.
2. I put right action before my need to win and be the best.
3. I live by my values in all circumstances.
4. I have the courage to tell the truth.
5. I let go of my fear about what others think of me.

Read Shay's story: Metal Element courage story p.112
Ask, "What does this story mean for you?" *[**cr**]with "I (*name the positive meaning*)" (*will be off/umb off*).

e. **Water Element**

(**mcs**) {1–5}. *[**cr**] *(will be off/umb off)*.

1. I have the courage to persevere round every obstacle.
2. I am calm in crisis situations.
3. I have the clarity of mind to see beyond the present fearful situation and find solutions.
4. I have the courage to use my willpower, energy and drive to keep moving forward.
5. I contain my energy in fearful situations so I don't use up my energy in fear and panic.

Read the Water Element courage story p.115
Ask, "What does this story mean for you?" *[**cr**]with "I (*name the positive meaning*)" *(will be off/umb off)*.

J. Identify the coherent SNS stress response needed

(**mcs**) (1–3) for the response needed to neutralize the fears and create new neural pathways for courage.

1. **The alert response**

   (**mcs**) {1–11}. *[**cr**] *(will be off/umb off)*.

   1. I am alert and ready for action.
   2. I am alert yet relaxed.
   3. I orient myself away from danger.
   4. I orient myself towards what is nourishing, bonding and supports my survival.
   5. I am curious.
   6. If no threat is present I immediately relax.
   7. I quickly locate where there is danger and who is involved.
   8. I am confident.
   9. (I am able to identify and meet any challenge • I access a range of possible options and positive responses).
   10. If there is no threat I release residual activated energy by moving, trembling or shaking out my body tension.
   11. I easily move through states of tense hyper-vigilance and relaxed alertness.

2. **The fight response**
   (**mcs**) {1–5}. *[**cr**] *(will be off/umb off)*.
   1. (I defend myself • I set clear boundaries with (power • strength • confidence • love • humor).
   2. I stand on my own two feet.
   3. I am ready to face any challenge with (clarity • focused attention • appropriate decision-making • excitement • the ability to see all sides of the situation).
   4. After meeting a challenge I dissipate any residual mobilized energy by (shaking • trembling • moving • walking • dancing).
   5. I share my success in handling a challenge with *(name person/others)* and relax into love-bonding once more.

3. **The flight response**
   (**mcs**) {1–4}. *[**cr**] *(will be off/umb off)*.
   1. I move away from dangerous situations.
   2. I am clear and oriented when facing a danger so I know the most constructive way to handle the difficulty.
   3. After successfully avoiding a threat I (shake • tremble • move) in order to dissipate any residual mobilized energy.
   4. After successfully avoiding a threat, I discharge excess mobilized energy by playing out different ways of successfully escaping and I share my success with *(name person/others)*.

K. **Identify what client wants instead of the fears**
   Ask, "What do you want instead of these fears?"
   *[**cr**] *(will be off/umb off)*.

L. **The Energizing Option of eight acupuncture points without needles for creating new positive neural pathways for courage, so old dysfunctional pathways for fear atrophy through lack of use**
   If you have studied Resonance Repatterning, you can muscle check which of these points is needed and for the details on whether to use the ColorYourWorld Torch, Tuning Forks or an essential oil.

For non-Resonance Repatterning people, you may use a finger contact on one or more of these points.

See ResonanceRepatterning.net > Home Study Course for Inner Cultivation

- **Earth Element, Stomach Meridian**: This point is about two inches below the knee crease on the outer edge of the leg. Slide your finger into the muscles towards your shin bone and see if you can feel the point.

  This point is called Leg Three Miles. The ancient Chinese Acupuncturists believed that this point supports longevity and revitalizes your energy. It is wonderful to use this point when you need endurance, stamina, stability and especially when you are worried about harvesting positive results from what you have done, or feel there will be no harvest for the work you have put in. This point will help strengthen your resolve to keep moving forward, keeping you grounded and energized for your onward journey.

- **Metal Element, Lung Meridian**: The point is under the clavicle where it meets the shoulder.

  This point is called Cloud Gate. It is uplifting, helping you reconnect to the Divine within yourself, to see through the clouds of difficulties, to have faith that the sun is still shining beyond the clouds.

- **Water Element, Bladder Meridian:** The point is on either side of your spine at the top of your neck, just under the ridge of your skull bone, on the large trapesius neck muscle. Your two fingers will be about an inch away from the spine, one on each side.

  This point is called Heavenly Pillar. It gives you the strength, power, calmness and energy to handle the resistance of your challenges and gives you the inner strength to keep reaching for your vision.

- **Wood Element, Liver Meridian**: The point is underneath the middle of the ribs on both sides.

  This point is called Gate of Hope. It gives you the hope, optimism and vision to handle your stress with positive action, coherent plans and decisions that are aligned with your vision.

- **Fire Element, Heart Protector Meridian**: with the palm facing up, the point is found on the middle of the wrist in the hollow that you can feel when you flex your hand towards you.

  This point is called Great Mound – the burial ground for emperors – a place of great power. Great Mound gives you a renewed sense of confidence, safety, trust and love when you are feeling vulnerable or when you need to call on the strength of your generational history for support and vision.

- **Fire Element, Triple Heater Meridian**: With your arm bent and the palm facing the shoulder, this point is about an inch above the tip of the elbow on the back of the upper arm.

  This point is called Heaven Well. It strengthens the mind and spirit by helping you recharge yourself through connection to the divine – an inexhaustible well that has only good to bring.

- **Fire Element, Heart Meridian**: This point is at your armpits, behind the tendon – children like to place their thumbs on these points!

  This point is called Utmost Source. It is a wonderful point to use when there is chaos, confusion, agitation or when you no longer feel oriented towards your vision. Do this point when you need to reconnect deeply to the ultimate source of love, compassion and consciousness within yourself.

- **Fire Element, Small Intestine Meridian:** This point is on the outer edge of the little finger just above the notch of the base joint of the little finger.

  This point is called Forward Valley. It gives you the drive and perseverance to transform life's problems into challenging adventures. It empowers you to sort out what is rich and to act on what enriches your life. It helps you move forward fearlessly and with will-power when you have much to sort out, helping you conserve your energy by doing what is important, and leaving the rest.

M. Bach Flower Essences Positive Action

If you have the Bach Flower Essences, you can use the appropriate Essence for this session in relation to the fear that emerged.

Choose the Bach Flower Essence for your primary fear category: Aspen, Mimulus, Red Chestnut, Cherry Plum, Rock Rose.

How to:
- Once you have decided on the essence you need, put two drops from the stock bottle into a clean dropper bottle and fill with pure spring water.

- Take four drops in a little water at least four times a day, or more often if you feel the need; or put a few drops into a liter bottle of spring water and sip during the day.

- Hold the dose in your mouth for a few moments before swallowing.

- If you have not noticed any beneficial effect within two weeks, you may need another essence. If you notice a beneficial effect, continue taking the essence as long as the need is present.

HOW TO USE THE FEAR TO COURAGE REPATTERNING IN YOUR DAILY LIFE
EVEN IF YOU HAVE NOT YET ATTENDED A RESONANCE REPATTERNING SEMINAR

- Whenever you go into fear, take a **two-second pause**: consciously create new neural pathways with an Energizing Option or a Positive Action (Bach Flower remedies, Acupuncture point, etc.). Be aware that when you refuse to indulge your fears (which are based on past experiences), those old neural pathways begin to atrophy from lack of use.

- Every time you go into fear, do something from the **Fear to Courage Repatterning**: the alert, fight-fight response section, the Bach Flower Remedy section or the Five Element section.

RR SESSIONS: If you would like to receive the complete Repatterning with a professional Resonance Repatterning Practitioner, in person or over the phone, go to ResonanceRepatterning.net > Sessions for RR Institute Practitioners worldwide who have listed themselves on the RRI website.

RR SEMINARS: If you would like to attend Resonance Repatterning seminars in person or online, so you can use RR effectively on yourself and/or others, go to ResonanceRepatterning.net > Seminars for the list of teachers endorsed by the Resonance Repatterning Institute to teach.

6. SELF-MASTERY
IN THE FACE OF PROBLEMS

Under physical and psychological attack, we discovered that
a flaw is corrected only by being revealed, and that the true
opponent is the one who resides within.

George Leonard, *The Silent Pulse:*
A Search for the Perfect Rhythm that Exists in Each of Us

STORY OF AIKIDO TRIAL BY FIRE

The following story shows what happens when we connect to spirit
by using our problems as a challenge, rather than collapsing under
their weight. It illustrates the power of self-mastery in relation to
any problem we may have to face.

"Aikido Trial by Fire" is extracted and summarized from *The Silent
Pulse* by George Leonard – a classic, first published in 1978, in which
he relates the extraordinary experience he and three others went
through while preparing for a black belt examination in aikido.

Leonard writes, "There were four of us, three men and a woman,
who shared an ordeal, a rite of passage.... Richard, Lawrence,
Wendy, and I – and over a period of about a year, each of us in our
own separate way confronted injury, exhaustion, humiliation, and
despair."

Leonard says of their aikido teacher, Robert Nadeau: "He is not
your run-of-the-mill martial artist.... He teaches us not to deny
or avoid tensions and problems and pain in our practice but to

welcome them as treasured gifts, as opportunities for transforming our lives. Far from working around our weaknesses, Nadeau zeroes in on every divided motive, every pretense, every secret well-guarded flaw.... It is a world beneath a magnifying glass, where nothing can remain long hidden. In this setting, self-examination is not mandatory; it is unavoidable."

The extraordinary event

In Leonard's own words he describes what happened.

"During the three-month period leading up to the black-belt examination...Nadeau uses this period ... as a physical and psychological trial by fire ... [having] a remarkable ability to know exactly in what technique each candidate is unprepared....

"(But) it was Richard's experience that seemed to draw us into other worlds, joining us with the immense and the infinite.

"In his early thirties, at the very prime and glow of life ... he seemed a modern counterpart of the classic Greek ideal of physical beauty.... Dazzled by his gifts and grace, we might find it hard to discover any flaws in this man.

"Nadeau told Richard that it was up to him – he could go through the three months of preparation if he wished. On the day of the exam, said Nadeau, he would let him know whether or not he would take it.

"For Richard, this was like a slap in the face. He would have to endure a three-month-long ordeal with no assurance of any reward at the end.... As the weeks passed, Nadeau paid less and less attention to him.... [He] never looked at Richard or called him by name.... In the shower room three days before the exam, I asked Richard what he thought was going on.

"'I don't know. I can't tell exactly. Something's happening to me. I'm beginning to feel some kind of transformation.'

"... The exam was scheduled on a Sunday at one.... People began gathering early: aikidoists from miles around, hundreds of spectators. An examining board of five ranking black belts would be convened to pass on the candidates' performances.... Richard went into the office and came out with a strange look on his face.

"'I guess I'm going to take it,' he said. 'I saw my name on the schedule. Nadeau still hasn't said anything.'

"... Five candidates had already been examined when Richard was called to the center of the mat.... He moved out in the graceful knee-walk common to the art. [With his attacker – called the uke – they] bowed first to O Sensei [the legendary founder of aikido], then to the five examiners, then to each other.

"... From the very beginning, it was apparent that something extraordinary was occurring ... an enactment in space and time of how the universe works, how things are.... The silence in the dojo became deeper and more vibrant. Nadeau called for the next series of techniques. The uke rose and attacked the still-kneeling Richard, who moved in sweeping circular motions to embrace the attack. So gentle and coherent were his movements that they seemed to capture time itself and slow it to a more stately pace.

"Nadeau called for the next series of techniques.... When Richard rose to his feet, there was a slight stir in the room; people here and there glanced up at the windows or the lights. What happened, inexplicably, was that the room had suddenly become appreciably lighter.

"... As the exam continued, the speed and intensity of the attacks increased, and yet there was still a general sense of time moving slowly, at an unhurried, dreamlike pace.... For his part, Richard was beginning to get the feeling that he was not 'doing' anything at all, that the movements of his body were 'just happening' without thought or effort.

"...When Nadeau called for the uke to attack free-style, the illumination in the room seemed to go up another notch and the boundary of light surrounding Richard seemed to become denser, brighter, and unmistakably golden. The genius of aikido is to transform the most violent attack, by embracing it, into a dance, and it was the essence of dance we saw there on the mat.

"Nadeau ... gave Richard a minute to catch his breath before the climactic randori, the multiple attack.... At this moment, we in the dojo experienced a third brightening of the room. By the time the three-man attack was in full swing, the whole place was alight as if from within with the most delicious, joyful, almost palpable illumination.

"To a first-time spectator, the rushing, swirling, tumbling, crashing motion of a randori is simply overwhelming.... But on this day spectators and experts alike saw Richard's randori as harmony.... No matter how hard or swift the blow, he was not there to receive it, but always at the moving center that holds all opposites in perfect tension.

"As for Richard, he experienced no effort or strain whatever.... There, in the eye of the storm, stripped of the certainty he had always deemed necessary for survival, denied the support of his teacher, divested even of his name, Richard found the deliverance he had not known he was searching for.... If need be, he could go on forever, realizing all the while that 'he' was not doing it."

Every problem is a gift

This story touches a place within that tells us what we already know on some level – that every problem is a gift, a treasure, of supreme power and learning, that however mundane our own problems may be, they are an opportunity for self-mastery, for transcendence even. To stand in the eye of the storm in our light, acting without acting, effortless effort.

We will explore this theme of self-mastery in relation to any problem we may have, and how Resonance Repatterning can help us move towards embracing our problems so we too move into a different way of being – into the dance, touching the edge of what is possible.

In the process of understanding the potential our problems hold for us, we will cover

- Six basic life problems that all of us may face at one point or another in our life

- Four aspects that hold our problems in place

- What is needed for self-mastery

- Extraordinary outcomes

Six basic life problems

1. **Health issues**: Besides poor health from poverty, chronic lack of food and birth process traumas, health issues are usually a result of poor lifestyle choices: poor food choices, over- or under-eating, lack of exercise, not drinking enough water, not having twenty minutes of sunshine a day on the body, lack of sleep and deep relaxation, in addition to pollutants from air, water and vaccinations – all of which can lead to poor health and disease.

2. **Money problems and integrity issues**: A lack of money, a misuse of money, a lack of integrity concerning how we earn and deal with money, an inability to save money or spend money appropriately, along with debts and being under-paid or over-paid for what we do.

3. **Work, power and control issues**: Work we don't like, work we would love to have but don't have, being underpaid for the work we do, lack of appreciation and respect at work, sexual harassment at work, lack of integrity at work, excess ambition at the cost of others' well-being, lack of cooperation and belonging at work, unresolved differences, lack of communication and listening, lack of fun and humor, overwork and being driven to the point of exhaustion, anger and reactiveness, boredom and lack of creativity, power and control issues, constraints that limit creativity and feeling forced to make decisions that lack integrity or are out of alignment with our values.

4. **Relationship difficulties**: A lack of friends or intimate relationship, control and power issues in relationship, infidelity and trust issues, lack of nurturing and respect, anger and quarrels, lack of kindness, thoughtfulness, fun, humor, shared interests, commitment and spiritual values; not having or using the tools to overcome the daily differences that arise in relationships.

    Mastering our problems is also about mastering our fear of people and how they respond or don't respond to us, based on our earlier experiences. As infants and children, our life depended on our caregivers – our parents and our family tribe. If our needs for love, bonding, growth, protection, open communication and a balanced life free of violence, abuse and alcoholism were not met, we felt our survival was threatened, or it may in fact have been threatened. And these unresolved patterns continue to be super-imposed on our present relationships.

5. **Mental-emotional states**: Negative thoughts, non-coherent beliefs, reactive feelings that do not uplift, depression and serious mental problems like multiple personality, Alzheimer's, dementia and autism. (These nervous system-brain disorders resulting in physical health issues like dementia, Alzheimer's, Parkinson's and Downe's syndrome, etc. have been improved through positive changes in life-style – diet, exercise, vision etc.).

6. **Spiritual challenges**: Inability to find the meaning and purpose of life, not following one's spiritual practice or living by its values, an inner yearning for God but not finding the path or practice, putting worldly priorities first

before spiritual priorities, a lack of disciplinc in practicing the spiritual way in the face of no results.

Looking at these six issues, we can see more clearly that mastering our problems is about mastering our self, embracing rather than ignoring or resisting our flaws under the magnifying glass of our life – knowing that every flaw will be revealed in order to challenge us to discover the next step in our inner transformation and the limitless possibilities within.

As a result of earlier experiences, our frequencies moved out of sync with our true nature – the coherent state of inner relaxation, acceptance, trust, balance, faith, energy, vision, peace, uplift and well-being – no matter what the external circumstances of our life may be. Each one of us is being challenged to center ourselves once more so we can move from our inner center, in the present timeless moment.

The four aspects of any problem

1. The conventional view of problems that most of us hold
2. The felt sense in response to our thoughts, beliefs and feelings about our problems
3. Fear reactions to our problems
4. Two negative attitudes towards our problems

1. The conventional view of problems that most of us hold

A problem is a symptom or a situation we have but don't want – something we view as unpleasant, painful or stressful; something we want to change or get rid of, but have not done so, otherwise we wouldn't still be stuck in our "problem." Or it may be a situation or something we don't have but want.

As long as we have this not wanting/wanting point of view about our problems, we will remain embedded in them – manifesting more of the same, with a few variations, for the rest of our life.

So the first step, which we use in Resonance Repatterning, is to change our resonance with the different aspects that go into making up our problem, because what we resonate with is what we will keep on experiencing. If we resonate with a problem, that's what we experience – a problem!

2. The felt sense

The second step is to get in touch with what we call our felt sense – whatever we feel in our body in response to our thoughts and feelings about our problem.

If we close our eyes and think about a problem, we'll observe certain tensions: a tight jaw, stress in the eyes, contracted or shallow breathing, hands sweating or clenching, an anxious feeling in the stomach.

This tension, sooner or later, can lead to physical symptoms: digestive troubles, chronic tension in the neck and back, joint pain, headaches, vision problems and even illness.

Tension and stress are where illness and pain start. And stress begins with the negative thoughts and feelings we resonate with. So a physical symptom is a clue telling us that we resonate with the out-of-sync frequencies of an unresolved problem. The symptoms themselves are rarely, if ever, the problem itself.

Tuning in to the felt sense brings an awareness of stress and tension, often before we are even conscious of the negative thoughts, beliefs and feelings causing the tension in our body.

3. Fear

The third step is to check whether we resonate with fear, which may be masked as anger, grief, depression, irritation and so on – all these emotions in one way or another having their basis in fear.

If Richard in the trial by fire story had gone into fear – fear that he wouldn't be able to take the aikido exam with his colleagues, fear that his teacher didn't like him, fear that there was something wrong with him that his teacher ignored him and didn't call him by his name, fear that he wasn't good enough – he would have dissipated his energy, stressed himself out and disconnected from "the field of all possibilities" that led to his extraordinary outcome.

Fear cuts us off from the field of all possibilities. Changing our resonance with our fear leads to a dramatic lift in how we feel – opening up the potential for courage, inner strength, confidence and the power to be our self and radiate our light.

An important understanding in relation to any fear is that our fear is based on a negative belief, thought or projection of our mind that we take to be true. Overcoming fear then, starts with letting go of the negative belief or thought that creates the feeling reaction we call fear.

One of our primary fears is that we are not perfect and therefore we are not capable of being loved or of loving. As a result of this fear, we try to conceal our flaws and mistakes, or we ignore them, resist them, hide from them. Transforming our lives involves the courage to embrace our flaws and our mistakes and reveal them to ourselves so we can discover the treasure of the next step in our transformation.

4. Two negative attitudes

The two negative attitudes that make it impossible for us to move out of any problem state are blame (and complaining) and hopelessness.

It is worth noticing in life how we constantly jump into one of these two attitudes: blaming someone – "He couldn't handle me... He has a problem... It is his/her fault... She betrayed me... She doesn't appreciate me" – or hopelessness: "He/she won't change... There's nothing I can do... It's just the way it is... I did it again – I'll never improve... I'll never achieve what I want."

Once we resonate with knowing that all our problems are our own personal responsibility and contain a treasure for us within their depth, we will no longer blame anyone or complain about something or someone "out there" causing our difficulties.

Confidence and self-transformation bring hope and right action. Then hopelessness and self-pity complaints cease to exist for us.

When we experience our problem as a messenger, telling us that a positive change is needed in our own out-of-sync frequencies, and when we change our resonance with those frequencies, we are finally free to move into empowered action.

Extraordinary outcomes

One of the most extraordinary things about the Black Belt story is that

- in spite of breaking his arm during the one-year preparation, Richard continued to practice.

- In spite of a broken cheekbone from an accidental kick, he kept going.

- In spite of his teacher ignoring him and never calling him by name, he persevered.

- In spite of his teacher not even telling him that he would receive the honor of taking the Black Belt examination until the actual day of the exam, he never gave up. He never complained. He continued his practice.

Richard stayed in the present moment of right action.

He followed his own inner vision, his light, through the discipline of the daily grinding practice.

He accepted the blows, the failures, the reality of his situation. He didn't waste time analyzing or discussing what was happening, thinking about what was happening, complaining about what was happening, resisting what was happening. He simply did the practice – he focused on his own right action.

He challenged himself to trust his teacher totally – that there was an underlying purpose for the "disrespectful" and "harsh" way his teacher was treating him. In other words, he trusted that what was happening was for his own good. He surrendered. He let go of every extraneous thought and feeling that was not his practice.

He avoided anything that depleted his energy: blame, criticism, hopelessness and judgments – all negative states that deplete our energy, block right action and obstruct access to the field of limitless possibilities.

Richard conserved his energy and focused his attention on his vision, on perfecting his practice.

The lesson for us

Our life is like a challenge to complete our own Black Belt training. We do this successfully when we:

- avoid giving up in the face of difficulties

- avoid depleting our energy with blame and complaints

- observe any tendency towards feeling hopeless and helpless, and get back to "What is right action here?"

- refuse to give in to the mind's projections that we are too weak, too inadequate, too overwhelmed and too undisciplined

What is enough

Just having a vision of what we most want – with no good or bad judgments about what life brings us – is enough.

Then, we hold firm to the actions that lead us toward our vision. That too is enough.

In these ways alone, we discover outcomes that are far beyond what we could ever have imagined.

No guarantees about what we will receive or when. But one guarantee is that extraordinary outcomes are always unexpected, not what we think will happen or even want to happen. Always better.

This is what we see in Richard's experience: the light and power that result when we hold to our inner path, no matter what is happening or not happening outside ourselves.

Extraordinary outcomes relate to being at the moving center, in the eye of the storm, where time is slowed down and action becomes effortless. Like Richard in the story, no matter how hard and swift the blows of our life problems, we are not there to receive them.

FURTHER READING

George Leonard. *The Silent Pulse: A Search for the Perfect Rhythm that Exists in Each of Us*. New York, NY: E.P. Dutton, 1978.

6.

SELF-MASTERY
REPATTERNING

SELF-MASTERY REPATTERNING

A. **Read or tell the story of aikido trial by fire** *p.137*
Ask, "What does this story mean for you?" *[**cr**]with "I (*name the positive meaning*)" (*will be off/umb off*).

B. **What you really want and the problem**
Do {a–e} in sequence.

a. *Ask,* "What do you really want? What goal do you want to realize that is most important to you?
*[**cr**] (*will be off/umb off*).

b. *Ask,* "What problem are you facing that comes in the way of realizing this goal?"
*[**cr**] (*will be on/umb on because at the moment client resonates with the problem rather than with the self-mastery needed for realizing the goal*).

c. **An area of stress**
(**mcs**) {1–24}. *Ask,* "How do you imagine this stress with (*name {1–24}*) relates to you and your problem?"
*[**cr**] (*will be on/umb on because at the moment client resonates with this underlying stress factor associated with the problem*).

1. Money
2. Mother
3. Father
4. Past trauma
5. Issue concerning spirituality
6. An issue with (*name someone who is difficult for you*)
7. Weight issues related to (birth trauma • womb stress • lack of protection • low self-worth • lack of love • infancy and childhood eating habits • anger • depression • lack of exercise • other)
8. Sleep issues
9. Depression
10. (Procrastination • Inability to act • Inertia)

11. Issue with (self-worth • criticism • public opinion • your own internal critic)
12. Addiction issues with (food • alcohol • drugs • sex • other)
13. Abortion issues
14. Sexuality issues
15. Power issues
16. Issue with lack of purpose
17. Letting go issues
18. Forgiveness issues
19. Issue with (lack of • excessive) ambition
20. Decision making issues
21. Issues around (anger • grief • fear • lack of joy • worry • other negative emotion)
22. (Fun • laughter • relaxation) issues
23. Issues with death and dying (your own • someone else's)
24. Work issues

d. The conflict

Ask, "Where are you in conflict in relation to (*name what is most important to client and what comes in the way* {*B a b*})? Or where are you not being true to (*name what is most important to client*)?"

*[**cr**] with "I am in conflict because (*name what is most important*) but (*name what comes in the way*)" *(will be on/umb on because at the moment client resonates with the conflict).*

Understanding the conflict and not being true to your need

Internal conflicts and not being true to ourselves and our deepest needs deplete our energy. For instance, a married woman with a husband and three sons gave all her energy to managing the family. However, her deepest longing was to paint. Then she got cancer. As her time was limited, she stopped doing everything for the family and began to paint. She cured herself of her cancer. We have to learn to do both: take care of our obligations and also be true to what is most important to us.

e. **The flaw that is concealed**
Ask, "What weakness or flaw in yourself do you feel or imagine might be connected to (*name the problem*)?"
*[**cr**] with the flaw *(will be on/umb on).*

*[**cr**] with "I (ignore • resist • conceal • justify • am unconscious) that (*name the weakness or flaw*) and as a result I am unable to transform and resolve my problem" *(will be on/umb on).*

C. Identify the felt sense
Do {a–b} in sequence.
a. *Ask,* "What negative feeling is associated with (*name the problem*)?"
*[**cr**] with, "I feel (*name the feeling*)" *(will be on/umb).*

Understanding the negative feeling
Every problem is held in place in the present by our resonance with a life-depleting, highly charged feeling associated with a past memory, even though at this point you may not be aware of what that memory is.

b. **Identify the body response**
Ask client: Close your eyes. Be aware of (*name the problem*). See it, feel it, hear it. Now observe where you are tense as you think of your problem. How is your body responding? Your heartbeat? Breath? Sweating? Jaw? Eyes? Stomach? Any other area? When you are ready, you can open your eyes.
*[**cr**] with "I go into a stress response of (*name the stress body responses*) (will be on/umb on).*

D. Identify the fear
Do {a–b} in sequence.
a. **The fear**
Ask, "What are you afraid of?"
*[**cr**] with "I am stressed out by my fear that (*name fear*) and there is no action I can do to alleviate my stress" *(will be on/umb on because at the moment client resonates with the fear and stress underlying the problem).*

Understanding the fear

Problems in the present are associated with a protection or trauma response of fear associated with a past experience. As in the past, we are still stuck in the belief that there is nothing we can do to alleviate or handle the present stress/fear situation we are in. As a result we cut ourselves off from the field of limitless possibilities, where every possible solution already exists, and from where our courage, inner strength and confidence can be accessed.

b. Earlier fear

Ask, "Does your fear that (*name the present fear*) remind you of a similar earlier experience?"

*[**cr**] with "I am still stressed out by my past experience of (*name the earlier experience*), which is activating my present problem and fear" (*will be on/umb on*).

E. Identify the negative attitude

(**mcs**) {1–2} for the one needed. Write down the statement.
*[**cr**] (*will be on/umb on*).

1. **The blame attitude**: (I am justified in my critical, judgmental attitude • I discharge my feelings of (frustration • anger) by talking negatively about (*name person*) • The situation with (*name the problem situation*) is (*name person*)'s fault • Other: *Ask,* "How are you blaming someone else for your problem?").

2. **The helpless attitude**: (In the face of my difficulty, all I can do is feel bad, complain and give up • There's nothing I can do • Life isn't fair • There's no point in trying to change this situation • (*Name person*) is the cause of this problem and I am helpless to change his/her mind • It's not my fault • I feel hopeless about a positive outcome • I keep complaining, but nothing changes • (*Name person*) isn't going to help me resolve this problem).

Understanding the negative attitude

Resonating with a non-coherent attitude, we inevitably stay in the darkness of blame and complaints, unable to manifest a constructive solution to our problem.

When we resonate with taking personal responsibility for the fact that all our problems reflect an aspect of our own internal reality, we no longer complain, blame or judge something or someone 'out there' for our difficulties.

We may not be able to change the situation itself. But resonating with a coherent attitude, we go into action to create positive change within ourselves. This gives us the energy to focus on right action, rather than feeling hopeless and helpless.

F. Self-Mastery

Do {a–h} in sequence.

a. Name the dynamic edge of conscious choice – your point of choice
Ask, "In relation to (*name the problem*), are you prepared to make a positive change in yourself? If you do, say aloud: "Yes, I want, choose and am ready to make a positive change in myself in relation to (*name the problem*)."
*[**cr**] (*will be off/umb off because client does not yet resonate with wanting, choosing or being ready for the necessary positive change*).

b. Name the positive change from within yourself that you need
Ask, "What positive change from within yourself do you need to make in order to (*name the goal {B a}*)?"
*[**cr**] (*will be off/umb off*).

Understanding what you really want and inner change

The more we think about our problems, the more it reinforces the same brain-body neural pathways for those problems. This makes these pathways stronger and more easily activated even by the smallest of triggers. Whereas thinking about what we want instead of our problems and our own positive change activates new neural pathways and connections between the higher brain prefrontal cortex and the emotional limbic brain. These new connections to the higher brain prepare us to go into action for what is most important to us – our priority – rather than remaining stuck in the external "problem.

c. **The positive feeling**
   Ask, "What positive feeling would you have if (*name the positive change {F b}*)?"
   *[**cr**] with "I feel (*name feeling*)" *(will be off/umb off).*

   Understanding the positive feeling
   The brain-mind wants pleasure. If we resonate with a positive feeling of pleasure, then we are motivated to do what it takes to activate the pleasure centers of our brain by doing what gives us pleasure. If we don't resonate with the positive feeling associated with what we want, we will tend to give up on doing the necessary actions for achieving what we want.

d. **Transcending fear**
   Ask, "Is your fear that (*name fear belief {D a}*) true?"
   *[**cr**] with "My fear of (*name fear*) is just a belief, and I easily let go of this fear belief" *(will be off/umb off because client does not yet resonate with the fear being just a belief – a thought projected from the mind – and being able to let go of this belief, which is depleting their energy and weakening their will).*

e. **Name the strength**
   Ask, "What inner strength or positive quality do you need that will help you (*name what client wants {B a}*) and will give you the willpower to handle (*name the problem {B b}*)?"
   *[**cr**] with "I am/have (*name the positive quality/strength*)" *(will be off/ umb off).*

f. **Taking responsibility**
   *[**cr**] with, "I take responsibility for (*name the flaw {B e}*) and the part I am playing in (*name the problem*)" *(will be off/umb off).*

g. **Acceptance and gratitude**
*[**cr**] with "I accept that whatever is not aligned with my vision for what I want to achieve/be emerges for my growth and transformation and I am deeply grateful for everything I experience in my life" *(will be off/umb off)*.

h. **Right action**
Ask, "What is one positive action you can do in this situation that will help you live your new possibility and make it your priority – so you can visualize it, imagine it, think it, manifest it and be grateful for it?" *[**cr**] *(will be off/umb off)*.

G. Extraordinary outcomes

(**mcs**) {a–h} for the one(s) needed. *[**cr**] *(will be off/umb off)*.
a. I live my vision/intention/goal in action every day, all the time.
b. I persevere with right action regardless of the obstacles.
c. I use my willpower to live good habits.
d. I trust that everything is happening for my own good.
e. I conserve my energy by focusing on the present moment of right action.
f. I (stop • control) my negative mind projections and thoughts.
g. I am receptive to the field of limitless possibilities.
h. I let go of visualizing outcomes I would like and trust that outcomes will be unexpected and different from anything that I can imagine.

H. The Energizing Option of eight acupuncture points without needles for creating new positive neural pathways for courage, so old dysfunctional pathways for fear atrophy through lack of use

If you have studied Resonance Repatterning, you can muscle check which of these points is needed and for the details on whether to use the ColorYourWorld Torch, Tuning Forks or an essential oil.

For non-Resonance Repatterning people, you may use a finger contact on one or more of these points.
See ResonanceRepatterning.net > Home Study Course for Inner Cultivation

- **Earth Element, Stomach Meridian**: This point is about two inches below the knee crease on the outer edge of the leg. Slide your finger into the muscles towards your shin bone and see if you can feel the point.

  This point is called Leg Three Miles. The ancient Chinese Acupuncturists believed that this point supports longevity and revitalizes your energy. It is wonderful to use this point when you need endurance, stamina, stability and especially when you are worried about harvesting positive results from what you have done, or feel there will be no harvest for the work you have put in. This point will help strengthen your resolve to keep moving forward, keeping you grounded and energized for your onward journey.

- **Metal Element, Lung Meridian**: The point is under the clavicle where it meets the shoulder.

  This point is called Cloud Gate. It is uplifting, helping you reconnect to the Divine within yourself, to see through the clouds of difficulties, to have faith that the sun is still shining beyond the clouds.

- **Water Element, Bladder Meridian:** The point is on either side of your spine at the top of your neck, just under the ridge of your skull bone, on the large trapesius neck muscle. Your two fingers will be about an inch away from the spine, one on each side.

  This point is called Heavenly Pillar. It gives you the strength, power, calmness and energy to handle the resistance of your challenges and gives you the inner strength to keep reaching for your vision.

- **Wood Element, Liver Meridian:** The point is underneath the middle of the ribs on both sides.

  This point is called Gate of Hope. It gives you the hope, optimism and vision to handle your stress with positive action, coherent plans and decisions that are aligned with your vision.

- **Fire Element, Heart Protector Meridian**: With the palm facing up, the point is found on the middle of the wrist in the hollow that you can feel when you flex your hand towards you.

  This point is called Great Mound. The burial ground for emperors – a place of great power. Great Mound gives you a renewed sense of confidence, safety, trust and love when you are feeling vulnerable or when you need to call on the strength of your generational history for support and vision.

- **Fire Element, Triple Heater Meridian**: With your arm bent and the palm facing the shoulder, this point is about an inch above the tip of the elbow on the back of the upper arm.

  This point is called Heaven Well. It strengthens the mind and spirit by helping you recharge yourself through connection to the divine – an inexhaustible well that has only good to bring.

- **Fire Element, Heart Meridian**: This point is at your armpits, behind the tendon – children like to place their thumbs on these points!

  This point is called Utmost Source. It is a wonderful point to use when there is chaos, confusion, agitation or when you no longer feel oriented towards your vision. Do this point when you need to reconnect deeply to the ultimate source of love, compassion and consciousness within yourself.

- **Fire Element, Small Intestine Meridian:** This point is on the outer edge of the little finger before the notch of the base joint of the little finger.

  This point is called Forward Valley. It gives you the drive and perseverance to transform life's problems into challenging adventures. It empowers you to sort out what is rich and to act on what enriches your life. It helps you move forward fearlessly and with will-power when you have much to sort out, helping you conserve your energy by doing what is important, and leaving the rest.

HOW TO USE THE SELF-MASTERY
REPATTERNING IN YOUR DAILY LIFE
IF YOU HAVE NOT ATTENDED
A RESONANCE REPATTERNING SEMINAR

When any problem comes up for you, do one or more of the following:

1. Become aware that you have a problem – whether it is a negative thought about a family member or someone you work with or a more obvious problem such as money problems you are anxious about. Know that if you are experiencing a problem, you resonate with it. If you didn't resonate with it, you wouldn't have the problem. Do an Energizing Option from SPIRAL UP! to change your resonance with the problem.

2. Get in touch with your felt sense concerning your problem. Observe how even the thought of your problem affects your breathing and creates tension. Notice where it creates tension. Do an Energizing Option to change your resonance with your problem and the felt sense physical sensations.

3. You can do {B a} and one or two other letters (for example, Fear and the Negative Attitude, or Self-Mastery letters plus an Energizing Option).

RR SESSIONS: If you would like to receive the complete Repatterning with a professional Resonance Repatterning Practitioner, in person or over the phone, go to ResonanceRepatterning.net > Sessions for RR Institute Practitioners worldwide who have listed themselves on the RRI website.

RR SEMINARS: If you would like to attend Resonance Repatterning seminars in person or online, so you can use RR effectively on yourself and/or others, go to ResonanceRepatterning.net > Seminars for the list of teachers endorsed by the Resonance Repatterning Institute to teach.

7. COMMITMENT TO YOUR SELF – CHALLENGE TO GREATNESS

The arts as they are studied in Japan … are not intended for utilitarian purposes only or for purely aesthetic enjoyments, but are meant to train the mind; indeed, to bring it into contact with the ultimate reality….

If one really wishes to be master of an art, technical knowledge is not enough. One has to transcend technique so that the art becomes an 'artless art'….

Man is a thinking reed but his great works are done when he is not calculating and thinking. 'Childlikeness' has to be restored with long years of training in the art of self-forgetfulness. When this is attained, man thinks yet he does not think. He thinks like the showers coming down from the sky; he thinks like the waves rolling on the ocean; he thinks like the stars illuminating the nightly heavens; he thinks like the green foliage shooting forth in the relaxing spring breeze. Indeed, he is the showers, the ocean, the stars, the foliage.

Daisetz T. Suzuki, Introduction to
Zen in the Art of Archery
by Eugen Herrigel

STORY OF THE KENYAN ATHLETE

Some years ago at the Olympic Games, there was a young athlete from Kenya running the marathon. He arrived in the stadium for his final stretch to the finish line after completing his twenty-six mile run – the clear winner. But before he could reach the finish line, he fell.

He managed to stand up again, but he couldn't walk or run. Clearly he was in agony. Then he did an extraordinary thing: hobbling forward, step by step, he slowly limped to the finish line. The thousands watching cheered him on, many in tears. Later when he was asked why he endured this pain to do what he did, he responded: "My country didn't send me here to start the race. My country sent me here to finish the race."

On one level or another each one of us wants to be challenged to greatness. Whoever we are, whatever our education and regardless of our earlier experiences of pain or pleasure, the spark of greatness is there within, waiting to be lit.

Greatness is like a beacon that we recognize because it represents the shining of our light in this world. This kind of greatness represents an ideal that we all yearn to achieve in our own chosen way, because we want to access, express and share our light. Greatness, this light, represents self-mastery that goes beyond winning and losing.

Finishing the marathon for the young Kenyan was his commitment to himself; it was his challenge to greatness. No one now remembers who won that race. But everyone who has seen the film of that young athlete remembers him, and is still moved by his inner victory.

STORY OF COACH CARTER

In the film *Coach Carter*, we see a man who was committed to his own kind of greatness and became a light for others.

In this true story, Coach Carter decides to take the underpaid job of coaching a failing high school basketball team, in an underprivileged school in a down-and-out neighborhood where

36% of the eighteen to twenty-four year olds end up being arrested and 80% of the population is more likely to go to jail than to college. The school only graduated 50% of its high school students and only 6% of those – mostly girls – went on to college.

But Coach Carter had a vision for the basketball team – that they could develop their gift for basketball, study so they could go to college on scholarship and create a different life for themselves.

If they didn't attend class and maintain a C grade point average, he wouldn't let them play basketball, however good they were at basketball or however much the team needed them to play. Standing by this value meant facing opposition from the school board, the parents, the teachers and the media. But he stood his ground for greatness and refused to give in.

Finally, six of the boys, so close to failure in life, ended up going to college on full scholarships: a first in that high school.

～

What is this power of commitment – to ourselves and the challenge to greatness that it makes possible for us? Why is it that most of us are only using 3% of our brain or only manifesting 10% of our potential? How can we give 100% of ourselves to our life and open ourselves to infinite possibilities?

Know your gift

The first step in the challenge to greatness is to know and recognize our gift.

- What do we love to do and want to do more than anything else?

- What have we always wanted to do?

- What is our bliss, as mythologist Joseph Campbell called it?

For one person it may be achieving physical health and vitality; for another it is playing an instrument or singing; for another it is dancing; or a spiritual practice; or something on the computer; or being a healing practitioner; or gardening, painting, acting, writing, creating a business that will make a difference. Each of us has something we have always wanted to do – a talent or interest that motivates us to learn and grow and achieve our own inner greatness.

Human beings are capable of almost anything. When we fail to discover our gift and manifest our light, when we deny what we want in life, we tend to become ill or feel tired or stressed out, angry and frustrated. This is why each one of us needs to ask, "Am I living the life I came here to live?" and "What gives me joy?" Eating, paying bills, doing daily chores, making phone calls, watching TV or going to the movies take very little brain power and none of these motivate us to manifest our true potential.

When we challenge ourselves to greatness we need a lot more than 3% of our brain. Opening ourselves to what we want to be and live activates new neural pathways and multi-millions of neural connections.

12 obstacles to manifesting our potential

There are twelve basic obstacles that stop us from manifesting the gift of our greatness.

1. **Laziness:** If we are lazy, we won't love our gift enough to put in the daily practice – the hard work. Living our greatness does involve work – joyful work, but work nonetheless! Achieving our potential involves making our gift a priority. We need to make big demands on our self to activate the greatness that exists within and is waiting to emerge.

2. **Fragmentation:** We give 1% of ourselves to this, and 3% to that and perhaps 6% to something else. We multi-task to such an extent that we lose our ability to focus on one thing. We split ourselves into pieces and then wonder why we can't bring much of what we do to completion.

People who achieve their greatness give 100% to everything they do: 100% to washing the dishes, 100% to playing with their children, 100% to their work, and yes, 100% to developing their gift – and living with purpose.

3. **Tension:** In everything we do, we are holding too much tension – tension in our eyes and face muscles, our neck and shoulders, our arms and hands and our mind. If we observe ourselves when we sit down or walk from one room to another, we will see how much needless tension we are holding onto. It takes a lot of energy to hold our muscles in a state of tension, and most people have chronically tight muscles that never let go! Our tension leaves us tired or exhausted, with no motivation to exert ourselves in developing our gift.

4. **Fear of our power:** Marianne Williamson writes, "Our deepest fear is not that we are inadequate. Our deepest fear is that we are powerful beyond measure."

   In Chinese Five Element Acupuncture, fear and power are associated with the Water Element. The power of the Niagara Falls is definitely scary, overwhelming and awe-inspiring. To manifest our power, we need to be able to contain it so, like water on a lake, it is serene and gentle. If our Water power is too strong, we need to bring it into balance. We need to discover and resonate with our inner tranquillity, our peace of mind. In this way we can show up powerfully in our life without misusing or wasting our energy or overwhelming others with our uncontained energy.

5. **Lack of focus:** Whatever is achieved in life, whether a musical or artistic gift, success in computer programming, writing or a spiritual practice, focused attention is essential. Without focus, nothing is achieved.

6. **Poor habit patterns:** There are numerous things we do in the day that we can do automatically – same action, same time – rather than re-thinking repetitive actions each day. Good habit patterns save energy. Good habits give us the discrimination to know what actions are important and which actions we need to discard. Poor habit patterns waste precious energy that we need to devote to what is most important to us.

7. **Wasting energy**: To manifest our potential, we need to observe how we spend our energy and on what. Where are we wasting our energy? What do we need to do to conserve our energy and recharge our battery reserves of energy?

8. **Tiredness**: It takes energy to manifest our talents and gifts. We need to make sure we recharge our brain and all our trillions of cells with good sleep, exercise and healthy food choices. If not, tiredness – a lack of energy – will stop us from manifesting our potential.

9. **Losing heart in the face of failures**: It is easy to lose heart when we fail. If we want success, or the achievement of our vision, we need to put in effort. And efforts inevitably lead to failures as we discover what works and what doesn't, and what new learning we need to integrate. Only hope, faith and optimism will see us through our failures, keeping us motivated to put in yet more right effort. Our heart must be with us, holding a confident belief in ourselves, regardless of whatever failures we go through. Losing heart in the face of failure is one of the great obstacles we must overcome.

10. **Lack of perseverance**: Perseverance is another quality that helps us through every failure. One of the most difficult things to do is to learn from our failures and keep on improving. When Edison was told that he had failed nine hundred times to create an electric light bulb and perhaps it was time to give up, he responded that he hadn't failed nine hundred times, he had simply learned nine hundred times what didn't work. Without perseverance, we will achieve nothing.

11. **Misdirected desire**: Achieving our potential involves focusing on what is most important. Money, name and fame, having a big house and material objects, are not what motivate or manifest greatness. In fact, wanting outcomes of any sort is a misdirected desire. Attaining our potential is about something very different. It is attuning to our true nature, manifesting who we are and the higher qualities of mind and spirit. Outcomes are not in our hands. As we let go of desires of any kind, outcomes happen by themselves.

12. **Time is not used for manifesting the gift**: Whatever we want in life takes time. We may have an extraordinary gift, but if we aren't willing to give time to manifesting it, nothing will be achieved. And time, like sand, has a way of pouring through our fingers.

Awareness plus changing our resonance with non-coherent, out-of-sync frequencies opens us up to infinite possibilities. Once the boys in the **Coach Carter** story recognized that their coach stood for their greatness, they got the confidence to study and as a result they received the help they needed so all of them as a team passed their exams. And they were changed for life.

The fourteen qualities for manifesting our potential

There are fourteen qualities that we see in those who manifest greatness through their chosen talent, practice or longing.

1. **Play the court** is the first quality of greatness. In the film *Coach Carter,* the high school basketball team has been accepted for the state finals but is pitted against the best team in the state. His kids are not doing well. On a break, Coach Carter tells them to "start playing the court": they are being run around; they aren't deciding any play; they are not in control. The boys rise to the challenge and they take control of the game.

   In life there's a tendency when we are not coming from our greatness to feel the victim of life and circumstances. We are running around, out of control. Where are we not deciding any of the plays in our life, practice and gifts?

   Although the team lost the game, Coach Carter tells them: "There's not always a fairy story ending, but you played like champions. You achieved what many people spend their life trying to achieve: victory." So for us in our life, playing the court is about self-mastery – not about winning or losing. As Coach Carter tells the boys, "Act as champions, play as champions, be champions." Our challenge to greatness is to live our vision in this way.

   Whatever we want to achieve, we must *be* that, as though it already is.

2. **Discipline with love** is another essential for manifesting our greatness, no matter in what area of our life – spiritual, mental, creative or physical. Manifesting our potential takes daily practice at the thing we most love to do. Without love for what we do, we will give up when difficulties emerge. Discipline without love is empty of joy and love without discipline takes us nowhere. We need both: discipline with love.

3. **Relaxation** is the third quality for manifesting our greatness. It's about using the least effort – effortless effort – free of all excess tension in the body, emotions and mind.

4. **Perseverance** is the fourth quality. Perseverance sees us through our off-days when we lose heart and want to give up, when it's raining, too hot or too cold, and we don't feel like doing what we have committed to do. As athletes say, "Feeling doesn't come into it. You just do it." This is perseverance.

5. **Patience** is a quality coupled with perseverance – patience to put in full effort free of frustration in the face of no results or our inability to achieve the outcomes we want.

6. **Right attitude – that failure is not an option.** "There is no such thing as failure," said Thomas Edison, the great inventor, "*only something new and exciting to learn.*"

   Like Apollo 13, stuck in outer space without enough fuel to bring the three astronauts back into the earth's atmosphere: the scientists said they could find only enough fuel to bring them halfway home. The head of the NASA project told them, "Halfway home is not an option." And they did the impossible.

   Halfway is not an option for us. If we cannot embrace failure as a learning, we will soon give up – usually with resentment and anger at someone else, blaming them for our giving up on our bliss, rather than taking responsibility for making our pain at failure more important than manifesting our greatness.

7. **Equanimity** is the seventh quality. Whether it is learning the art of archery in Japan, or playing basketball, or meditation, or being a healing practitioner and

teacher, equanimity is one of the most important of all the greatness qualities. It represents the eye of the storm, the unmoving center of peace amidst turmoil and emotional uproar. It means maintaining our center when we are criticized and blamed – and perhaps more important, when we are praised.

Equanimity is about recognizing that the energy of light from within that pours through us is what creates every success. The credit is not ours. Poise allows us to keep our center when circumstances present us with a challenge.

For example, there was once an Olympic race when a mistake was made as the gun went off. Three times the runners had to return to the starting line. They were visibly upset, frustrated, angry, pacing. Only one man kept his equanimity. He sat down cross-legged on the grass and waited patiently for the order to line up once more. No surprise that he won the race. His poise won the race for him; no wasted energy.

8. **Body position and movement** is the eighth quality of greatness. Whatever gift or talent we are devoting our lives to, each has a body position. For instance, if contemplation or prayer is your bliss, you can't sit with a slouching back and fidget. If it's singing, this gift has a definite stature. Playing the piano, ballroom dancing, giving a speech, manifesting health, self-confidence – all have their own form, body position and movement (as does sickness, depression and anger). Without the appropriate position, energy is out of sync with what we want to achieve and be. Without the appropriate body position and movement, there is no power and commitment behind what we are doing and we tend to weaken, get tired and give up.

9. **100% focus in the present moment, free of all distraction** is the ninth quality of greatness. Whatever greatness is achieved, no matter in what area of our life, it is achieved through focused attention. Thinking other thoughts, having regrets about what we have done or not done, fantasizing about the past or future, having negative thoughts, takes a large amount of energy and distracts from the moment of power in the present.

10. **Confidence** is the tenth quality of greatness – the confidence to overcome our self-doubt and know that anything is possible, that we are capable of almost anything. Confidence gives us a sense of hope – that all will be achieved and our only task is to practice, give our best and keep putting in our efforts to make the next quantum leap in our process.

11. **Letting go** is another quality of greatness: letting go of everything that comes in the way of greatness – whether boredom, anger, upset, fear, doubt, loneliness, plans and strategies, lack of forgiveness, resentments or tension. Letting go involves transforming all non-coherent out-of-sync frequency patterns that waste our energy, so our frequencies are amplified and focused on what we are to be and do.

12. **No complaints** is another quality of greatness. Complaining about what is changes nothing and wastes energy. It is like complaining about the weather: too hot, too cold, too wet. Nothing will change, and we are left feeling de-energized. Mahatma Gandhi never complained about being put in prison: for him it was an opportunity to write!

    No complaining means we either accept the situation as it is, or we go into coherent action to actively change what can be changed.

13. **Selflessness** is one of the most important of the qualities of greatness. Power and success can overwhelm and puff us up with our own self-importance, or we may try to keep ourselves small so we are acceptable to others. Again, Marianne Williamson:

    > Your playing small doesn't serve the world.
    > There is nothing enlightened
    >   about shrinking so that other people
    >   won't feel insecure around you.
    > We were born to make manifest
    >   the glory of God that is within us.
    > It is not just in some of us.
    > It's in everyone.

Selflessness keeps us humble: what has a hose pipe to be proud of? It is simply a hollow tube made in such a way that water flows through it. When we live with mastery, the creative power that flows through us enables us to play big, and even to receive the credit, but selflessness keeps our ego in check. We are nothing but an empty hose pipe – a hollow tube with a role to play.

14. **Surrender** is the most difficult of all the qualities and comes only after a lifetime of disciplined and loving practice. Surrender allows us to let go of our desires; it is about self-forgetfulness, accepting every situation as God-given. Being a witness to the energy of life flowing through us and doing all is surrender. In athletics this peak moment is called the Flow or being in the Zone: all is done seemingly without any effort on our part.

So Surrender is a moment of effortlessness when we do nothing and experience that all is being done through us rather than by us.

Surrender is the arrow flying by itself to the mark.

STORY OF EUGEN HERRIGEL AND THE ART OF ARCHERY IN JAPAN

In *Zen in the Art of Archery*, Eugen Herrigel, a German philosopher, spent four years studying archery in Japan. What held him back from his greatness was his desire for outcomes: he wanted the arrow to hit the target – *#11 Misdirected desire!*

His teacher said it was unimportant whether the arrow hit the target or not. The only thing of importance was his practice: holding the bow (symbolic of his inner focus) with the least amount of effort and tension, totally relaxed, and then simply letting go. Year after year: effortless effort, relaxing, letting go, focus. His teacher told him that one day the arrow would fly by itself to the mark: "The archer hits the target without having aimed."

Herrigel's teacher tells him that he must see the target as though he had not seen it. And in the practice hall one evening the teacher demonstrates what he means.

He tells Herrigel to light a thin taper and place it in the sand in front of the target. He then instructs Herrigel to turn out the lights. In the pitch darkness Herrigel can no longer see the target. But his Master shoots an arrow and Herrigel can hear that it has hit the target. Then his Master shoots another arrow. When Herrigel turns on the lights he sees that the first arrow is lodged in the middle of the target and the second arrow had splintered the butt of the first, plowed through its shaft and lodged itself next to the first arrow. Finally Herrigel understands that the archer does in truth hit the target without having aimed.

It is the same in our spiritual practice and all other creative or athletic practices: no desire for outcomes, no desire to hit the target. Simply the day-in, day-out practice: effortless, free of tension, totally relaxed, focused, year after year, letting go.

Our commitment to this kind of daily practice makes us receptive to infinite possibilities, and the energy of life does everything else. We commit, practice and let go.

So far we have looked at three aspects that lead toward manifesting greatness:

- Knowing our gift

- Transforming our resonance with the obstacles that stop us from achieving and being

- Resonating with and living the fourteen qualities for manifesting our potential

The fourth and final aspect is unhesitating action

Without action there is no mastery, there is no greatness – only fantasy. When we have an intention and a positive feeling and then go into unhesitating action (especially if we create a new habit by going into action every day for at least thirty days to anchor new neural pathways in the brain and body), it gives our feeling limbic brain and our thinking prefrontal cortex the message that our intention is possible. Our brain will then do everything to make our vision possible. Visualizing success plus unhesitating action reinforces that anything is possible.

Unhesitating action that creates new neural pathways also has its requirements:
- We need to practice doing what is most important to us every day.

- We need to give our focused attention to our practice.

- When we fail, we conserve our energy by being free of judgments. We enjoy the process of learning what doesn't work and discovering what does work. As Edison said, failure is about "new and exciting things to learn." And dealing graciously with failure at every step in our progress is a lifetime process.

- We need to be grateful for every second we give to our practice. And when we succeed, even more gratitude: I'm a hose pipe and by the grace of God a little of the water of life flowed through me.

Seven symbolic actions that support greatness

There are at least seven actions that support us in our journey of manifesting our gifts, no matter what that gift is – whether basketball or gardening or inner contemplation. Some of these seven actions appear to be totally unrelated to our gift and what we want to manifest. But in the greater sphere of things, each is significant.

1. **Clean the house:** Our home is a metaphor for our mind and body. Feng Shui demonstrates how clutter – what we don't use, what is untidy or messy, what isn't ours and what is broken – de-energizes us, confuses our thinking and blocks the flow of chi energy in our life.

2. **Relaxation:** Constantly practice holding the least amount of tension possible. Keep your body toned and flexible, but relaxed. This is something we can practice when sitting or walking, at home, at work, and especially when practicing our gift. Observe where you are holding unnecessary tension – in your hands, feet, legs, face, etc. – and let go.

3. **Breath:** Our breath reflects our emotional state. Often we hold our breath, we fail to breathe in or we breathe haphazardly. Smooth, relaxed and steady breathing is energizing and keeps us emotionally toned and vital. Practice consciously breathing during the day, and see how much more energy you have at the end of the day. Use the SPIRAL UP! Breath Energizing Options often. Breath generates the vital force we need to do what we want to do.

4. **Posture:** How we hold ourselves is a reflection of our inner strength and balance. How we sit or stand has an emotional correlation that affects us: cross our arms and we may feel protected or defended, but we may also feel closed off; stand on one leg, and most of us will be off center. It is important to stand and sit free of all tension (but not slouching) in our stature of power. Stand and move as a champion – relaxed, toned, alert.

5. **Give your best:** In any action you do, give it your best whether to washing dishes, exercising, listening to someone or attending a seminar. Nothing is inconsequential and there are no inconsequential relationships. When we live this, then we will also give our best to our chosen gift.

6. **Complete one thing at a time:** Either complete one thing at a time or give yourself a certain amount of time to do something, and when that time is over move on to the next thing. Practice 100% focused attention on what you are doing – committing 100% to each thing. Then when you practice your gift, you will have the attention and commitment for that too.

7. **Strengthen your body:** Whatever we achieve is through the vehicle of our body. It is essential to strengthen the house of our body with daily exercise, healthy organic foods (vegetables, fruits, seeds, quinoa, millet, amaranth, beans, lentils), drinking enough water and if possible drinking organic vegetable juices.

All of the above are integrated into the **Challenge to Greatness Repatterning** that follows.

FURTHER READING

Eugen Herrigel. *Zen in the Art of Archery*. New York, NY: Vintage Books, 1971.

FILM

Coach Carter. 2005.

7.

CHALLENGE TO GREATNESS REPATTERNING

CHALLENGE TO GREATNESS REPATTERNING

A. **Know the gift**

   Do {a–c} in sequence.

   a. **Identify the gift**

      Ask, "What is your gift – something you would love to devote yourself to with body and mind for the rest of your life, or something you are devoting yourself to but you'd like to do more?"

      *[**cr**] with "I devote myself body and mind to (*name the gift*)" (*will be off/ umb off*).

   b. **Identify the problem in relation to the gift**

      Ask, "What problem do you have in relation to your gift or doing what you most love and want to do?"

      *[**cr**] (*will be on/umb on because client resonates with manifesting the gift as being a problem*).

   c. **The negative belief**

      Ask, "What negative belief do you have in relation to your gift or doing what you most love and want to do?"

      *[**cr**] (*will be on/umb on*).

B. **Identify the twelve obstacles that stop client from manifesting his/her potential greatness**

   (**mcs**) {a–l} for the one(s) needed.

   a. (**mcs**) **Laziness is involved?** (I am lazy • I don't love my gift enough to put in the daily practice and hard work • I don't like what managing my gift demands of me).

   b. (**mcs**) **Fragmentation is involved?** (I don't give myself 100% to anything I do • I am unable to bring things to completion • I give myself 100% to other things, but not to what is most important to me • I give 1% of myself to this and 3% to that, but never 100% • I multi-task to such an extent that I can't bring much of what I do to completion).

c. (**mcs**) **Tension is involved?** (I am tense • My tension leaves me tired so I don't have the energy to do what is important to me • My tension leaves me tired/exhausted).

d. (**mcs**) **Fear is involved?** (I am afraid I am inadequate • My deepest fear is that I am powerful and I won't be able to contain my power • I am afraid I will overwhelm people with my power • I am afraid I will misuse or abuse my power).

e. (**mcs**) **Lack of focus is involved?** (I am not focused enough to (*name gift {A a}* • I don't bring focused attention to (*name the gift {A a}*) • My attention is scattered • While (*name gift*), I think of other things/ fantasize • I multi-task to such an extent that I lose my ability to focus on one thing).

f. (**mcs**) **Poor habit patterns are involved?** (I use poor habit patterns or addictive behaviors to avoid doing (*name the gift*) • I don't create good habit patterns that I can do every day automatically without thinking • I waste my energy re-thinking actions that I should be doing automatically • I don't know what actions are important and what actions I need to discard • I don't do those actions that are important and leave those that can wait for another day).

g. (**mcs**) **Tiredness is involved?** (I am not recharging my brain and all my trillions of cells with good sleep, exercise and healthy food choices • I feel tired • I don't have the energy to manifest my potential) • I am tired from using up my reserves of energy in (my work • upsets • my worries • frustration • handling my pain • anger • the daily routine • other).

h. (**mcs**) **Losing heart in the face of failure is involved?** (I lose heart when I fail • I give up and feel hopeless when I fail • I cannot accept that failures are inevitable • I judge myself harshly when I fail and this gets in the way of my enjoyment and focus • I lack the hope and optimism to see me through the inevitable failures that happen • I lose heart in the face of what others say and think when I fail • I cannot tolerate failure).

i. (**mcs**) **Lack of perseverance is involved?** (I lack perseverance (when the going gets tough • when I don't see results • when I don't feel like doing something) • I don't persevere in exploring what does and does not work).

j. (**mcs**) **Wasting energy is involved?** (I waste my energy in easy pleasure from (food • sex • entertainment • reading books • watching movies • playing video games • texting • being with people • other) rather than using my energy for (*name the gift {A a}*)• I don't notice where I am wasting my energy • I don't conserve my energy and recharge my battery reserves).

k. (**mcs**) **Misdirected desire is involved?** (I want outer success rather than inner transformation and mastery • I want signs of success for every small effort I put in • I focus on outcomes rather than on my efforts • I want (money • name and fame • to have a big house and material objects) rather than focusing on manifesting my potential)

l. (**mcs**) **Misuse of time is involved?** (I give my time to other things, rather than to (*name the gift*) • I resist giving the necessary time to (*name the gift {A a}*) • I waste time • I waste time doing things of no importance).

C. The earlier experience

Do (a–c) in sequence.

a. **Earlier experience**
Ask, "What earlier experience did you have that relates to (*name {B a–l}*)?"
[cr**] with "(Name the earlier experience*), and this obstacle from my past stops me from (*name the gift {A a}*)" (will be on/umb on).

b. (**Mother • Father) issue**
Ask, "Did your (mother • father) have a similar experience to yours {*B a–l*}? How does his/her issue relate to your (*name the gift {A a}*)?"
[cr**] with " I do what my (mother • father) models instead of (*name the gift {A a}*), which is what I want" (will be on/umb on because you have embodied your (mother's • father's) experience).*

c. **Identify what client would like instead**
   Ask, "What would you have loved as a child in relation to *{B a–l}*?"
   *[**cr**] with "My (mother• father) (*name what you would love*) and this
   supports me now in (*name the gift {A a}*) (*will be off/umb off*).

D. Identify the need to achieve your best, go beyond your limits and manifest your potential
(**mcs**) {1–13}. *[**cr**] (*will be off/umb off*).
   1. (I achieve my best • I value those who help me achieve my best).
   2. (I manifest my potential • I am successful • I enjoy going beyond the limits of what I thought was possible).
   3. I have the strength and faith to persevere through obstacles and apparent failures.
   4. I accept that achieving my dream has its ups and downs, involves hard work and brings its own hard knocks.
   5. I serve (others • humanity).
   6. I play (joyfully • spontaneously).
   7. I am curious.
   8. (I create beauty • I am creative in everything I do).
   9. I am confident.
   10. I am courageous.
   11. I maintain an optimistic attitude no matter what difficulties I'm facing.
   12. I put my concern for human well-being and right action before my need for (material success • the achievement of my ambitions).
   13. Other: *Ask,* "What do you need that would allow you to manifest your potential, go beyond the limits of what you think is possible and achieve your best?"

E. Identify the need for meaning, purpose, love and happiness from within
(**mcs**) {1–24}. *[**cr**] (*will be off/umb off*).
   1. (I feel joyful • I let go of all negative thoughts and tune in to love).
   2. I am filled with gratitude every day.
   3. I persevere with focused attention.

4. I commit myself 100%. I name my goal with confidence, no matter what others think.
5. I appreciate the synchronous events that let me know I am going in the right direction.
6. I am openhearted and friendly, and divine help comes to me naturally through the help of others.
7. (I see beauty • I see the Divine) in every aspect of the creation.
8. I am content.
9. (I have faith • I trust that every experience is for my highest good).
10. I am (focused • disciplined).
11. (I pay attention to my thoughts and the stillness of my mind • I am still).
12. I accept the divine will, free of resistance and fear.
13. I let go. I get out of the way and let God.
14. I live my (truth • values) in action.
15. I love unconditionally.
16. (I stand for what is right • I live with integrity).
17. (I practice the presence of God • I feel spiritually connected at all times to the Divine within).
18. I let go of (self-importance • negative thoughts and feelings).
19. (I am at peace • My mind is peaceful).
20. (I am receptive to divine grace).
21. (I serve selflessly • I give generously • I find every opportunity to help others).
22. I stay conscious of the light within and the light within each person I meet.
23. I am receptive to the higher purpose and meaning of every circumstance life brings.
24. I let go of my need to get (upset • angry • worried) about anything in this world. I trust. I have faith.

F. Motivation

Do {a–b} in sequence.

a. *Ask,* "What happy memories do you have that are associated with (*name the gift*)?"

*[**cr**] with "My happy memories of (*name the memories*) motivate me to (*name the gift {A a}*)" (*will be off/umb off*).

b. *Ask,* "What are you grateful for?"
*[**cr**] with "My gratitude for (*name it*) motivates me to (*name the gift {A a}*)

G. The fourteen challenges to self-mastery

Do (a–c) in sequence.

a. Read or tell the **Coach Carter** story *p.162*
Ask, "What does this story mean to you?" *[**cr**] with "I (*name the positive meaning*)" (*will be off/umb off for the positive meaning*).

b. (**mcs**) {1–15} for the primary one needed.
*[**cr**] (*will be off/umb off because at this time client does not resonate with self-mastery in relation to the gift*).

  1. (I take control and 'play the court' free of feeling a victim of life and others • I call the shots, feeling in control • I am free of feeling a victim of my feelings, urges and desires • I act as a champion, play as a champion and I am a champion).
  2. I am disciplined in my practice and do it with love.
  3. (I relax and release all excess tension • I feel light as I move into effortless effort).
  4. (I persevere through the bad days and enjoy the good days • I persevere by just doing it, no matter how I feel).
  5. I am patient in the face of no outcomes, no positive results and failures.
  6. (Failure is an opportunity for something new and exciting to learn • I avoid complaining about and feeling upset by my failures).
  7. (I maintain my poise and equanimity when criticized • I go beyond the need for praise • I allow energy to pour through me unhindered • I don't waste any energy by losing my center of poise).
  8. I maintain the physical alignment that supports manifesting my potential in (*name your gift*).
  9. I am focused in the present moment of action, thinking without thinking, free of past regrets and future fantasies, free of all distractions.

10. I am confident that anything is possible.
11. (I let go of everything that comes in the way of manifesting the power of my spirit • I let go of wasting my energy on non-essentials • I let go of what is not love).
12. (I avoid complaining about anything • I accept what is and go into right action • I am content).
13. I have the courage to accept my power, and express it with gentleness or with drive according to what is appropriate in each situation.
14. (I give my best • I surrender to the Divine, accepting the higher will in all things).
15. I maintain my balance, free of pleasure in success or upset over perceived failures.

c. Read the story of **The art of archery** *p.171 Ask,* "What does this story mean to you?" *[**cr**] with "I *(name the positive meaning)*" *(will be off/umb off for the positive meaning)*.

H. Commitment to unhesitating action
Do (a–b) in sequence.
a. Read or tell the story of **the Kenyan athlete** *p.161*
Ask, "What does this story mean to you?" *[**cr**] with "I *(name the positive meaning)*" *(will be off/umb off for the positive meaning)*.

b. (**mcs**) (1–6) for the one needed.
*[**cr**] *(will be off/umb off)*.
1. I practice *(name the gift/talent)* (every day • with focused attention).
2. I love giving my attention and time to *(name the gift {A a})*.
3. I receive pleasure from my practice and feel energized doing it.
4. I enjoy that I am practicing for my own self-mastery and transformation, and to realize my fullest potential as a human being.
5. I am deeply grateful each time I *(name the gift {A a})*.
6. I persevere until I reach *(name the gift {A a})*.

I. Identify the positive action that is needed

(**mcs**) {1–7} for the positive action that supports the achievement of (*name the gift*).

*[**cr**] *(will be off/umb off because you do not yet resonate with this symbolic action supporting you in manifesting your gift).*

1. I clean my house, getting rid of clutter, what I don't use, what isn't mine and what is broken.
2. I consciously relax my body during the day, so I am holding the least amount of tension possible.
3. My breathing is slow and steady.
4. I maintain a posture that reflects inner strength, poise and equanimity.
5. I do my best in every situation and let go of the need for praise and my fear of criticism and blame.
6. I complete one thing at a time, or I give the allotted time before moving to the next priority.
7. I keep my body strong and healthy through exercise, right food choices, water, sunshine, sleep and meditation/contemplation.

J. Identify the Energizing Option needed

(**mcs**) for the Energizing Option from the SPIRAL UP! book that is needed for shifting the resonance patterns identified in this Repatterning.

If you are a Resonance Repatterning practitioner, you will then recheck the *[**cr**] statements to confirm the change.

HOW TO USE THE CHALLENGE TO GREATNESS REPATTERNING IN YOUR DAILY LIFE
EVEN IF YOU HAVE NOT YET ATTENDED A RESONANCE REPATTERNING SEMINAR

- Use the Fourteen challenges to self-mastery {G b 1–15}. (**mcs**) for the one you need and then do an Energizing Option so you resonate with it.

- Morning, afternoon and evening do some slow deep relaxed breathing.

- It is always a good idea to take a few parts of a Repatterning, one or two letters you feel drawn to, and then do an Energizing Option to change your resonance.

- Gradually you can do different combinations of the letters in short mini-sessions.

RR SESSIONS: If you would like to receive the complete Repatterning with a professional Resonance Repatterning Practitioner, in person or over the phone, go to ResonanceRepatterning.net > Sessions for RR Institute Practitioners worldwide who have listed themselves on the RRI website.

RR SEMINARS: If you would like to attend Resonance Repatterning seminars in person or online, so you can use RR effectively on yourself and/or others, go to ResonanceRepatterning.net > Seminars for the list of teachers endorsed by the Resonance Repatterning Institute to teach.

8. LIVING YOUR DREAM

At the heart of each of us, whatever our imperfections, there exists a silent pulse of perfect rhythm, a complex of wave forms and resonances, which is absolutely individual and unique, and yet which connects us to everything in the universe. The act of getting in touch with this pulse can transform our personal experience and in some way alter the world around us.

George Leonard, *The Silent Pulse: A Search for the Perfect Rhythm That Exists in Each of Us*

"If you don't follow through on your dreams you might as well be a vegetable."

"What kind of vegetable?" the small boy asked.

(Pause) "A cabbage – you might as well be a cabbage!"

From the film *The World's Fastest Indian*

Seeing our dreams as if they already exist, fully realized, is important for us and others too: when we live our dreams in action, something extraordinary begins to happen. Hearts are touched, lives change; the universe responds. And this isn't pie-in-the-sky thinking. It is based on people's experience throughout time.

We don't need to be extraordinary to live our dreams. We just need a few pointers – a friend to model that it is possible, against all odds.

STORY OF BURT MUNRO AND SPEED WEEK

Burt Munro is an older guy – maybe in his 60s, perhaps older. He has heart trouble, prostate trouble, hearing problems. He lives on a small pension in his garage with his 'Indian' motorcycle, and his dream – which is to go from New Zealand, where he lives, to the Bonneville Salt Flats in Utah, to compete in what is known as Speed Week.

For twenty-five years Burt has tinkered with his Indian motorcycle, getting it to go faster and faster – cutting the treads off the tires with his neighbor's carving knife, filling in the cracks in the tires with black shoe polish, welding this and that together.

Burt is a maverick – there is nothing conventional about this man who urinates on his lemon tree each day because he doesn't like to waste the best fertilizer in the world.

He doesn't care what his suburban neighbors think. He is who he is and he has a dream that he knows will come true. Month by month he has saved from his retirement check for the journey to the USA. Now he has only five days left before a small boat leaves for Los Angeles, and he still needs $2,000.

His friends think he is crazy – that he'll never get to Utah, and if he does he certainly won't break a record on his old motorbike. Only the little boy next door believes he can do it. Somehow or other Burt – in this true story – gets the money: gifts from his friends, from a gang of motorcyclists and a loan from the bank with his so-called house as collateral.

Burt gets a free passage to Los Angeles working as the ship's cook. But arriving in Los Angeles, his problems begin. "Why are you here?" the customs officer asks him. "To set a world record on my motorcycle," he responds. One look brands the old man as suspicious. He is questioned by other officers, until one of them recognizes him as the Burt Munro on a motorbike magazine cover he happened to have seen.

The amazed customs official stamps his passport and Burt moves on to his next adventure. At every step of the way his innocence, his genuineness, his directness, and his dream, win people over. Their outer shell begins to crack; they soften and they want to help him.

Driving a $200 rattletrap car with a trailer behind carrying his Indian motorcycle, he is on his way to the Bonneville Salt Flats. Then, in the middle of the desert the trailer tire drops off and his motorbike is lying in the bush. He has no spare tire, little money and time is running out.

After sometime a truck stops and a Native American gets out to help him.

Synchronous events

When you have a dream, synchronous events can be expected. Burt Munro is sensitive to these signs that confirm his dream and tell him he is on the right track – whether it's the bank manager's receptionist, whose last name is Springfield, the place where Indian motorbikes are made, or whether it's alone in the desert when the trailer tire bursts and he is helped by a full-blooded American 'Indian', or the good luck charm his Indian helper gives him.

Facing all kinds of obstacles, Burt makes it to the Bonneville Salt Flats only to be told that he hasn't registered so he cannot enter his bike. Friends he has made try to help him, trying to persuade the authorities to bend the rules. Besides the rules, the authorities are also worried: his bike is twenty-five years old, it has been welded together out of bits and pieces, it has no brakes, he has no parachute, and if he gets killed they'll have problems.

Finally they agree to let him have a trial ride with two cars following behind him to make sure he doesn't fall off. They think that 75 miles per hour will be the limit of this ancient Indian motorbike, which could only do 50 mph when it was brand new, more than two decades earlier. Burt starts off across the salt flats, his bike weaving from side to side until he manages to straighten it out. The cars follow behind, his new friends laughing and disbelieving – who is this man!

Gradually Burt goes faster and faster and to their amazement hits 150 miles an hour. But at that point his bike begins to wobble dangerously and the only way he can stabilize the bike at high speed is to stand up – dangerous to say the least with the hot desert winds on his unprotected face.

With doubts and misgivings, the authorities finally agree to let him ride: the old geezer has come all the way from New Zealand and he has dreamed of this moment for twenty-five years. The rules get bent.

The big day arrives. Popping his angina pills, kissing his Indian charm, he is pushed off from the starting line by his friends. Burt wobbles from side to side and then once more manages to straighten out. Everyone is laughing, amazed. His dream lifts people's hearts.

The man in the booth begins to call out the bike's speed as Burt passes the check points: 100 mph; 150 mph; 175 mph. Everyone is listening in disbelief. How is it possible? 180 mph; 190. Burt's leg is burning from the smoking exhaust pipe. He stands up to stabilize the bike; his goggles are blown off his head and he is blinded by the wind.

Back in the booth the man becomes speechless – he can't even call out Burt's speed. He tries, but no sound comes out of his mouth. Finally he says: "201 miles per hour!" Everyone is laughing, hugging each other, jumping for joy.

So Burt broke the world record for the Indian motorcycle. At the end of the movie we are told that Burt Munro returned nine more times to the Utah Salt Flats – always testing himself to go even faster. In the 1960s he set numerous speed records, one of which still stands unbroken to this day.

Here was a man who lived his dream – no matter the burning exhaust pipe or being blinded by the hot desert winds without protective goggles.

There is no external reward for living your dream. As Burt tells the young boy – the child of his nextdoor neighbor – "The reward is in the doing of it." And he repeats a quote he loves from Roosevelt: The credit belongs to the one who is "in the arena."

Life for Burt Munro is about being in the arena, doing it, no matter what. After his first angina attack, the hospital doctor tells him his motorcycling days are over. Burt has no intention of taking this advice! Life is about living your dream. As he tells the small boy, "If you don't follow through on your dreams, you might as well be a cabbage."

What about 'ordinary' people

Even without talent we can dream the big dream. We might think to ourselves, "Well, Burt was gifted. He had a talent. He is different." But a dream is a dream, no matter who you are.

STORY OF A JAMAICAN
WITH AN EXTRAORDINARY DREAM

His dream was to run in the Olympics, but in the trials another runner tripped and fell, bringing him and a third runner down with him. So in spite of the young man's incredible speed, he was disqualified.

Seeing a photo of his father, a gold medalist sprinter in his time, standing next to a white man, he asks the chairman of the Jamaican Olympic committee who this white man was. The chairman tells him he was a two-time gold medalist bobsledder who lost his medals because he cheated in the Olympics. He had weighted his sled to make it go faster. He adds that he had a strange theory that the best bobsledders were sprinters, but he never had a chance to test his theory.

This is all the young Jamaican sprinter needs. Somehow or other he gathers a team of three other Jamaicans and persuades the out-of-shape former bobsledder gold medalist, who has given up on life, to be their coach.

- They have three months before the Winter Olympics

- None of the team has ever seen snow

- None of them has ever been in a bobsled, let alone faced the danger of the rollercoaster ride on a precipitous track made of ice.

They practice with an old four-wheeled cart surrounded by the blue tropical seas of Jamaica. Somehow they get the money together and land in Toronto in their bright Jamaican clothes, to be met by minus twenty-five degree weather. They don't even have a sled, but someone who owes something to their coach manages to lend them an old one, which they call 'Cool Runnings' – meaning: peace be on the journey.

They are the laughing stock of the German and Swiss teams with their expensive cutting-edge machines; the laughing stock of the media, who photograph them trying to catch up with their run-away sled in a practice session: their first time on ice.

Once more, obstacle after obstacle – the Olympic Alliance trying to disqualify them from competing by suddenly changing the rules and demanding that in the trials they must get to the finish line in a minute. Against all odds they succeed: they complete the run in 59 seconds, witnessed by a huge crowd that starts out laughing and mocking them and ends up astounded by their success and wowed by their spirit.

In spite of this success, they are still disqualified. Even the Jamaican Committee is embarrassed at the thought of their competing. But at the last minute they are given permission to compete.

Who they are, their dream, wins everyone's heart. Everyone is wearing Jamaican sweatshirts – even the two newsmen! The crowd cheers them on as they speed down the icy tunnel, looking like they will place in the top three and receive an Olympic medal.

And then almost at the end of their perfect run, something happens. A screw comes loose in the old bobsled, and they crash at tremendously high speed on the corner just before the finish line.

There is an appalled silence as the crowd looks at the inert bobsled – and then one by one, the four boys struggle out from underneath it and get to their feet. The captain says a word of encouragement and the four of them lift the bobsled and carry it slowly down the track to the finish line – winners of their dream to be in the Olympics.

As they cross the finish line everyone is clapping together in unison, honoring them and the power of their dream.

Know that 'I am enough'

At one point in the film *Cool Runnings,* the young Jamaican sprinter asks his bobsled coach why he cheated at the Olympics.

His coach tells him, "I made winning my whole life. When that's your life, you have to keep winning no matter what.... If you are not enough without your gold medals, you'll never be enough with them."

And the young sprinter asks him, "How will I know that I'm enough?" His coach tells him, "When you cross the finish line, you'll know." And as they carry their broken sled across the finish line – they know.

What we learn as we live our dream is that it's not about success or failure. It is about being in the arena, knowing we are enough, knowing that the reward is in the doing of it.

Living our dream is about being more than a cabbage!

The longing for oneness

When we dare to dream and dare to live our dream in action, no matter what the outcome in terms of success or failure – we radiate our light and the light of others becomes brighter. People get the fragrance of love. Strangers hug, filled with joy, and for that peak moment live with the knowledge that we are all one – we are all extraordinary. It's this opening to our innate oneness and magnificence that we are seeking.

Response from the field of limitless possibilities

George Leonard relates in *The Silent Pulse* that a man with the woman he loves is sharing a memory of being in the Air Force when he used to do acrobatic flying – telling her about the joy of doing snap rolls and loops in his Stearman biplane.

And then, on the beach a few minutes later, a movement in the sky: a lone biplane, a Stearman, coming straight towards them. It does a perfect snap roll, and pointing directly toward the couple again, it does another snap roll followed by a loop. Then the biplane disappears.

The extraordinary happens when we give up control by the ego and connect to the field of infinite possibilities through love – the basis of every dream.

When we are in tune, the universe responds with what we call miracles. Often these extraordinary synchronous events occur when there is intense love, or in a crisis, or in the total focus of competition, or in a state of total exhaustion when we can go no further, or when we are facing death. In a moment of transcendence, our normal ego-self lets go of its control – and we access the field of infinite possibilities where anything is possible.

That moment results in a sense of effortless effort, doing nothing of oneself, a sense of oneness – no separation. This is why people who live their dream have such a powerful effect on others. For a moment others too are lifted up by the dreamer's peak moment and they too feel whole, free of separation and experience the oneness between all beings with the joy this brings.

The extraordinary becomes commonplace

George Leonard says, "I learned aikido from a teacher who operates from the premise that the perfect move, the perfect throw, *already* exists. Our mission was simply to join it. Before we would be able to do so, we would have to practice long and hard, master the basics, take our share of bumps and bruises. But through all of this, the perfect throw would be there."

"Sometimes," Leonard writes, "I have my own students hold the vision or the feeling of a certain throw in their minds, and then practice it over and over again for an hour, until they are drenched with sweat and barely able to move. Too tired to try any longer, some of them undergo a kind of transformation. It's as if you could see their hesitancy and self-consciousness peeling off like old dead skin, and something radiant and newly energized emerging."

He ends: "For a while, the extraordinary becomes commonplace and relatively inexperienced students perform like masters."

See it, believe it 100%

So the perfect dream is already there, waiting for us to play our part: to sweat a little, master the basics, practice long and hard. But more than this, we must envision our dream as already realized. We must act as if it already is.

Arnold Schwarzenegger, who was Mr. Universe five times, said: "As long as the mind can envision the fact that you can do something, you can do it – as long as you really believe one hundred percent." He said that lifting weights must be done mentally before it can be done physically. He adds, "When weight lifters are standing in front of the bar they must, in their minds, lift it in order to then lift it physically. If they have one percent doubt, they can't do it."

Seven practical steps for living your dream

Let's look at seven practical steps that summarize what's involved in living your dream.

1. **Know what your dream is**, write it down and see your dream as already realized.

2. **See, visualize, that you *can* do it** – whatever it is you want to do and *believe* it 100%. Not even 1% doubt is allowable.

3. **Go into unhesitating action** towards realizing your dream – no matter what anyone says, no matter what obstacles may appear in your way or what the outcome may be.

4. **Face every obstacle**, allowing nothing to deter you from living your dream, knowing that you are in the arena of infinite possibilities where anything is possible.

5. **Give 100% of yourself** to realizing your dream even without knowing what the outcome will be. Burt Munro spent 25 years planning for Speed Week on

the Bonneville Salt Flats. He tinkered away at his motorbike every day – the daily 100%. The Jamaican bobsled team arrived in Toronto with no sled, no Olympic uniforms and no winter clothes, having never even ridden on a sled or seen snow before! But they were there, 100% ready to enact their dream.

6. **Allow for the unexpected**. What comes from the field of limitless possibilities is always unexpected, it is never what we think or imagine will happen. Put in effort, go into appropriate action and then allow whatever is to happen from the field of limitless possibilities to happen.

7. **Finally, accept and embrace every failure**. Every seeming failure is a motivation for more growth, more learning – a spark that keeps us moving onward to wherever our dream leads. Pablo Casals, one of the greatest cellists of all time, was asked why he still practiced the cello at the age of eighty. He said: Because there is always more to learn.

This is the humility of greatness – and the greatness of living our dream!

FURTHER READING

George Leonard. *The Silent Pulse: A Search for the Perfect Rhythm that Exists in Each of Us*. New York, NY: E.P. Dutton, 1978.

FILMS

Cool Runnings. 1993.

The World's Fastest Indian. 2005.

8.

LIVING YOUR DREAM REPATTERNING

LIVING YOUR DREAM REPATTERNING

A. **Read or tell the story about Burt Munro and Speed Week** *p.190*
Ask, "What does this story mean for you?" *[**cr**]with "I (*name the positive meaning*)" (*will be off/umb off*).

B. **Identify the dream**
Do {a–e} in sequence.
a. **Identify the dream you want to live and realize no matter how long it takes you**
Ask, "What is your dream – something you want to achieve or be, no matter if it takes you the whole of your life?"

*[**cr**] with, "I work towards my dream of (*name your dream*) no matter how hard the work, what the obstacles, what the failures. I am in the arena. I have total faith that my dream will come true in the time destined from the field of limitless possibilities" (*will be off/umb off because at this time client doesn't resonate with living the dream for life, whether achieving it in two seconds, a few years or over a lifetime*).

Understanding the importance of the dream and stating a time
In a Princeton University study, one-third of the students wrote their five-year plan down; another third had a plan but did not write it down. The group that wrote down their plan achieved what they wrote within five years. The group that had a five-year vision but did not write it down, did not achieve their vision. *Have client write down their dream.*

b. **Envision the dream**
Say, "Close your eyes. Now see in detail, free of all doubt, your dream as realized."
*[**cr**] (*will be off/umb off because client doesn't resonate with visualizing the dream*).

c. **Identify the positive feeling**
    Ask, "If you achieved your dream of (*name the dream*), how would
    you feel?"
    *[cr] with, "On the way to achieving and manifesting my dream,
    I constantly feel (*name the feeling*)" (*will be off/umb off because at this
    time client doesn't resonate with the pleasurable feeling that motivates client
    to keep going no matter what and that makes the dream real in the present
    moment even before it has been realized*).

d. **Identify the inner strength needed**
    Ask, "What inner strength or quality would help you most on the way to
    achieving your dream of (*name the dream*)."
    *[cr] with, "I constantly tap into my inner strength of (*name the inner
    strength*) in order to keep persevering towards realizing my dream" (*will
    be off/umb off because client doesn't resonate with the inner strength*).

e. **Identify the positive projections needed**
    Ask, "What positive thoughts or projections do you need to have?"
    *[cr] (*will be off/umb off because client doesn't resonate with the positive
    projections or beliefs that make all things possible*).

C. **Identify the underlying need your dream motivates you to fulfill
    and live**
    (**mcs**) {a–b} in sequence.
    a. The need to achieve your best, go beyond your limits and manifest your
        potential
        (**mcs**) {1–13}. *[cr] (*will be off/umb off*).
        1. (I achieve my best • I value those who help me achieve my best).
        2. (I manifest my potential • I am successful • I enjoy going beyond the
            limits of what I thought was possible).
        3. I have the strength and faith to persevere through obstacles and
            apparent failures.
        4. I accept that achieving my dream has its ups and downs, involves hard
            work and brings its own hard knocks.
        5. I serve (others • humanity).

6. I play (joyfully • spontaneously).
7. I am curious.
8. (I create beauty • I am creative in everything I do).
9. I am confident.
10. I am courageous.
11. I maintain an optimistic attitude no matter what difficulties I'm facing.
12. I put my concern for human well-being and right action before my need for (material success • the achievement of my ambitions).
13. Other: *Ask,* "What do you need that would allow you to manifest your potential, go beyond the limits of what you think is possible and achieve your best?"

b. The need for meaning, purpose, love and happiness from within (**mcs**) {1–24}. *[**cr**] *(will be off/umb off).*
1. (I feel joyful • I let go of all negative thoughts and tune in to love).
2. I am filled with gratitude every day.
3. I persevere with focused attention.
4. I commit myself 100%. I name my goal with confidence, no matter what others think.
5. I appreciate the synchronous events that let me know I am going in the right direction.
6. I am openhearted and friendly, and divine help comes to me naturally through the help of others.
7. (I see beauty • I see the Divine) in every aspect of the creation.
8. I am content.
9. (I have faith • I trust that every experience is for my highest good).
10. I am (focused • disciplined).
11. (I pay attention to my thoughts and the stillness of my mind • I am still).
12. I accept the divine will, free of resistance and fear.
13. I let go. I get out of the way and let God.
14. I live my (truth • values) in action.
15. I love unconditionally.
16. (I stand for what is right • I live with integrity).

17. (I practice the presence of God • I feel spiritually connected at all times to the Divine within).
18. I let go of (self-importance • negative thoughts and feelings).
19. (I am at peace • My mind is peaceful).
20. (I am receptive to divine grace).
21. (I serve selflessly • I give generously • I find every opportunity to help others).
22. I stay conscious of the light within and the light within each person I meet.
23. I am receptive to the higher purpose and meaning of every circumstance life brings.
24. I let go of my need to get (upset • angry • worried) about anything in this world. I trust. I have faith.

D. Identify the negative projection involved

Ask, "What negative thoughts or projections do you have in terms of realizing your dream?"

*[**cr**] *(will be on/umb on because right now client still resonates with these negative projections that come in the way of persevering action).*

E. Identify the earlier experience that has created non-coherent neural pathways for living and manifesting the dream

Do {a–e} in sequence.

a. The experience

Ask, "What earlier experience did you have when you doubted yourself?"

*[**cr**] with, "(*Name the earlier experience of self-doubt*)" *(will be on/umb on because at the moment client still resonates with this self-doubt in the present).*

b. Negative feeling

Ask, "What negative feeling did you have in that earlier experience?"

*[**cr**] with "I continue to feel (*name negative feeling*) in the present, which blocks the pleasure of living my dream" *(will be on/umb on because client still resonates with this negative feeling that stops him/her from having pleasure in living the dream in the present).*

c. **The negative belief**
Ask, "What negative belief about (yourself • others • life) do you imagine you had as a result of that experience and your feeling of (*name the feeling*)."
*[**cr**] *(will be on/umb on because client still resonates with believing this thought as though it were true).*

d. **The meaning of the negative belief**
Ask, "What is the meaning you attach to this negative belief about (yourself • others • life)? If this is your belief, what does it mean?"
*[**cr**] *(will be on/umb on because client resonates with this meaning, which holds him/her back and sets limits on anything is possible).*

e. **New memory-thought imprint**
Ask, "What do you want instead of this memory imprint?" *Explain:* "It's all in your mind. You can activate new brain-nerve pathways for what you want. So what do you want instead of that memory?"
*[**cr**] *(will be off/umb off because client doesn't resonate with this new positive memory-thought).*

F. **Identify the belief that blocks realization of the dream**
(**mcs**) {1–21}. *[**cr**] *(will be on/umb).*
1. My dreams are impossible to realize.
2. I am too weak-willed to go into unhesitating and persevering action to fulfill my dream.
3. I am only worthwhile if I get quick results or win.
4. If I don't get results, I give up.
5. I have to lose my integrity if I want to win.
6. I allow others' praise to boost my ego self-worth and I allow their criticism to diminish my ego self-worth.
7. No one believes my dream is possible and I lose faith in myself.
8. It's easier not having a dream than having one and failing to realize it or making a fool of myself trying to realize it.
9. I let go of my dream when the going gets tough.

10. I can't be bothered to put in the hard work of achieving my dream over the years of my life.
11. (I try to please others and be what they want me to be, and I stop pleasing myself by living my dream • I am self-conscious of others' reactions to me, so I'm not myself and can't go for my dream).
12. I am overwhelmed by the obstacles I meet.
13. I lose hope.
14. I am lazy.
15. I waste my energy (feeling depressed • feeling a failure • getting angry • feeling afraid • through worries • through my non-coherent habits • other).
16. My dream embarrasses me – it is stupid and impossible.
17. There's no one to help me realize my dream.
18. I don't have enough love and passion for my dream.
19. My dream is too preposterous to realize.
20. I feel I have to manipulate to get what I want and where I need to go.
21. I don't trust the field of limitless possibilities to evaporate all obstacles one by one.

G. Identify the positive beliefs that will help you live your dream

Do (a–b) in sequence.

a. (**mcs**) {1–20}. *[**cr**] *(will be off/umb off because client doesn't yet resonate with this coherent belief).*

Ideally client needs to resonate with each of the following coherent beliefs. Return to this **Repatterning** *on a regular basis and check what other belief you need to resonate with on that day.*

1. I follow my dream and I live my dream no matter what.
2. I am 100% committed to believing in my dream and that anything is possible.
3. I believe in myself. I believe in my dream. One day when the time is right my dream is realized.

4. I am myself and who I am is enough, whether I win or lose.
5. I am honest and direct in my dealings with others and connect from my heart.
6. I am at peace on my journey.
7. I do what I most want to do, following my north star.
8. I am in the arena, living my truth.
9. I am good enough.
10. I put in 100% unhesitating effort, and then some.
11. I meet every obstacle with trust that there is a solution and that I will always receive the help I need.
12. I keep going no matter what others say and believe.
13. I live and act with integrity.
14. My heart is pure and innocent. I let my light shine.
15. I am unstoppable.
16. When called upon, I go beyond my normal limits of what I think is possible.
17. I follow my dream no matter how preposterous it may appear to be.
18. My heart and my dream inspire others to live with joy and to find their dream.
19. I live my dream to my last breath.
20. My reward is in (the effort to live my dream • being in the arena).

b. Read the Jamaican bobsled story *p.193 Ask,* "What does this story mean for you?" *[**cr**] with "I (*name the positive meaning*)" *(will be off/ umb off for the positive meaning).*

H. Identify the 100% commitment needed
Do {a–d} in sequence.
a. Identify the five actions
Ask, "What five actions do you need to take to realize your dream?"
*[**cr**] with, "I am 100% committed to (*name the five actions*) free of all hesitation" *(will be off/umb off because client doesn't resonate with the five actions that support the realization of the dream).*

b. **Accept the consequences**
Write down, "I face every obstacle on the way to realizing my dream and I keep persevering with (patience • inner strength • integrity • acceptance of the divine will)."
*[**cr**] *(will be off/umb off).*

c. **Let go of outcomes**
Write down, "I accept every failure as I persevere in right action, leaving all outcomes in the hands of the Divine/the field of limitless possibilities."
*[**cr**] *(will be off/umb off because client doesn't resonate with accepting every failure as part of the journey towards realizing the dream, and letting go of expected outcomes, which naturally emerge in their own way and at the right time from the field of limitless possibilities).*

d. **Allow for the unexpected**
Write down, "At every step of realizing my dream, I allow for the unexpected. I accept that what emerges from the field of limitless possibilities is for my growth and transformation and that of others. I let go and trust in God/the limitless field."
*[**cr**] *(will be off/umb off because client doesn't yet resonate with the unexpected, or with the unexpected occurrences on the way to achieving the dream as being a necessary part of client's growth and transformation).*

I. **Identify the Energizing Option needed**
(**mcs**) for the Energizing Option from the SPIRAL UP! book that is needed for shifting the resonance patterns identified in this Repatterning.

If you are a Resonance Repatterning practitioner, you can then recheck the *[**cr**] statements to confirm the change.

HOW TO USE THE LIVING YOUR DREAMS REPATTERNING IN YOUR DAILY LIFE
EVEN IF YOU HAVE NOT YET ATTENDED A RESONANCE REPATTERNING SEMINAR

- Do one or more of your five actions as much as possible – daily is preferable. Practice makes perfect, once you resonate with them.

- Write down your dream and visualize it as already realized. Have it on your desk. Look at it. Think it, feel it, see it. Re-inspire yourself with an Energizing Option.

- Change your resonance with every negative belief on the list that stops you from realizing your dream and resonate with every positive belief that helps you to realize your dream by doing Energizing Options for them.

RR SESSIONS: If you would like to receive the complete Repatterning with a professional Resonance Repatterning Practitioner, in person or over the phone, go to ResonanceRepatterning.net > Sessions for RR Institute Practitioners worldwide who have listed themselves on the RRI website.

RR SEMINARS: If you would like to attend Resonance Repatterning seminars in person or online, so you can use RR effectively on yourself and/or others, go to ResonanceRepatterning.net > Seminars for the list of teachers endorsed by the Resonance Repatterning Institute to teach.

ABOUT THE AUTHOR
AND THE RR WEBSITE

Chloe Faith Wordsworth, the founder and developer of Resonance Repatterning®, is the author of QUANTUM CHANGE MADE EASY, SPIRAL UP! 127 ENERGIZING OPTIONS TO BE YOUR BEST RIGHT NOW and ten Resonance Repatterning manuals. She lives in Arizona and teaches in the USA and abroad.

For more information go to *ResonanceRepatterning.net*

- To find **a practitioner** and to **advertise yourself as an RR Practitioner**, go to *ResonanceRepatterning.net > SESSIONS TAB*

- For **seminars** go to *ResonanceRepatterning.net > SEMINARS TAB*

- For information on Resonance Repatterning **books and Spiral Up supplies**, go to *ResonanceRepatterning.net > STORE TAB*

- For **Home Study courses** go to *ResonanceRepatterning.net > HOME STUDY TAB*

- To **listen free** to Chloe's LIVING IN TUNE web radio shows, go to *ResonanceRepatterning.net > LIVING IN TUNE TAB*

ACKNOWLEDGMENTS

Much gratitude to the authors of the books whose stories I have shared in LIVING IN TUNE WITH YOUR LIGHT and the authors of the quotes at the beginning of each chapter. I hope readers will enjoy and appreciate these books as much as I have.

My thanks to Yvonne Bost-Brown who volunteered to check some of the original web radio shows to make sure I hadn't left out any ad lib parts of importance. To Judith Urbina for persevering in her insistence that I write this book and create a new Resonance Repatterning seminar. And to Bobbie Martin whose email of gratitude for the Weight Repatterning (in another book in this series!) galvanized me into action. Many thanks to all of you for being my motivation.

Much appreciation to Anthea Guinness for copy-editing each chapter and being there when I needed to discuss the Repatternings; to Carol White for preparing the document for publication, correcting my inconsistencies and creating the book cover design; and to Leslie Pascoe Chalke for translating LIVING IN TUNE WITH YOUR LIGHT into Spanish – deep gratitude.

With thanks to Rose Jones for the photo on the front cover.

Continued appreciation to the Resonance Repatterning community – the students and practitioners who use Resonance Repatterning to make a difference in their own lives and the lives of others, and the RR teachers who are dedicated to passing on this work with joy and commitment.

Finally and most important, constant gratitude to my spiritual teacher and his successor for the light they bring and fill us with.

Made in the USA
Las Vegas, NV
01 August 2022

52492431R00122